C000146469

Diabetes, Food, Meds and More
is published by the InDependent Diabetes Trust.

© InDependent Diabetes Trust
PO Box 294
Northampton
NN1 4XS

ISBN 978-0-9928977-0-3

Designed and Printed by Flexpress, Leicester. 0116 267 6269

This book is written as a result of listening to people with diabetes and their families who contact the InDependent Diabetes Trust [IDDT]. It is increasingly obvious that many people feel insecure and unsure about the food they should or should not be eating when they have diabetes. This particularly applies to people with Type 2 diabetes many of whom appear to receive standard advice of eat a healthy diet and often do not have access to dietary advice from a dietitian.

Our experience is that healthy eating means different things to different people and despite views that people should not feel restricted by having diabetes, many people prefer to be given more direction about their diet, especially at the time of diagnosis, for special occasions or if they are unwell.

We know from personal experience that providing family meals when someone in the family has diabetes can cause anxiety, so we hope that this book makes life a little easier.

Note: All the recipes and exchange values have been checked by Dr Mabel Blades, a qualified dietitian.

"Any successful diet is about helping people to enjoy foods and fitting this into their lifestyle. This is why I loved writing this book."

Dr Mabel Blades

Introduction

Please could we ask you to read this introduction before venturing further into the book. The aim of this book is to help people with diabetes and their families to understand more about living with the condition with an emphasis on lifestyle, dietary information and recipes. However, it is not a typical recipe book, as it aims to cover real life, day to day situations. We differentiate between lifestyle essentials and lifestyle choices.

The book not only includes everyday meals but also what to eat if you are ill, when you are taking exercise, if blood glucose levels are low, if you are travelling or if you are having a party. It also has sections for people with diabetes and coeliac disease, a lifestyle essential, and for vegetarians and vegans with diabetes, lifestyle choices. It is a book to dip into when necessary rather than to read from cover to cover.

The book aims to cover:

- **Management** – the different types of diabetes and information on lifestyle issues.

- **Medication** – the ways Type 1 and Type 2 diabetes are treated, including information on different types of meals and how these link with insulin, medication and physical activity.

- **Meals** – recipes and ideas for meals and snacks, including those for special occasions.

People with diabetes or pre-diabetes, are often told that they need to eat healthily and while this is not bad advice, it can leave people feeling confused and without the information they need, at what can be a stressful time.

We hope the book will provide ideas and information to help with diabetes management, recipes for everyday, for special occasions and for times when meals and snacks need to take into account specific circumstances, such as exercise, hypoglycaemia, sick days and much more. We hope too that it will be of help to family and friends of people with diabetes, who often worry about what meals to provide for visits.

The information contained in 'Food, Meds and More' is not intended to be a substitute for individual care plans prepared by a dietitian or other health professionals but to provide a general overview of the relationships between the cornerstones of diabetes management – medication, diet and exercise.

Notes

Throughout this book we use the terms blood glucose levels and blood sugars interchangeably to reflect the terminology often used by people with diabetes. There is a glossary of terms at the back of the book to provide a quick reference guide to terminology such as this.

Chapter 1

The different types of diabetes

Diabetes is a chronic condition that affects around 3 million people in the UK, around 90% of whom have Type 2 diabetes and the remaining 10% have Type 1 diabetes. In the UK there are about 23,000 children with Type 1 diabetes aged 15 years and under. Type 1 diabetes is usually diagnosed as an acute condition but Type 2 diabetes can remain undiagnosed for several years. During this time, the blood glucose levels are too high which can cause some of the complications of diabetes.

Type 1 diabetes

- This type of diabetes accounts for about 10% of the total number of people with diabetes. It usually affects children and adults up to the age of 40, although some people are diagnosed with Type 1 diabetes when they are above this age, but this is relatively rare. It is sometimes still referred to as insulin dependent diabetes or juvenile diabetes.

- Type 1 diabetes is caused by the body's immune system attacking its own insulin-producing beta cells in the pancreas. This results in the body no longer producing insulin and the blood glucose levels rise. It is an autoimmune condition and treatment with insulin injections is always required for survival.

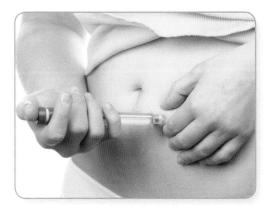

- There is no cure for Type 1 diabetes and the cause has not been established. It is thought that there may be several causes including a genetic link in some people and that a common virus may trigger the immune system to attack its own insulin-producing pancreatic cells.

Type 2 diabetes

- Type 2 diabetes affects about 90% of the total number of people with diabetes, over 2.5 million people, and it is thought that there are many thousands of people with undiagnosed Type 2 diabetes.

- In Type 2 diabetes the insulin-producing cells in the pancreas either do not produce enough insulin or the insulin they do produce cannot be used properly by the body (this is called insulin resistance). This means that the body cannot control blood sugar levels properly and gradually blood sugar levels rise (hyperglycaemia).

- Type 2 diabetes usually affects people over the age of 40 years but it can occur in people under this age.

- Type 2 diabetes can sometimes be treated with diet and exercise alone, sometimes with the addition of medication and if this fails to reduce the blood glucose levels sufficiently, then treatment with insulin is necessary. [Other injectable drugs to treat Type 2 diabetes are now available but they should not be confused with insulin.] Type 2 diabetes is a progressive condition which means that over time, blood sugar levels tend to rise.

- There is a tendency for Type 2 diabetes to run in families but a sedentary lifestyle and being overweight or obese are also causes.

Gestational diabetes

This type of diabetes may occur during pregnancy but disappears after the baby is born. Like other forms of diabetes, gestational diabetes affects the way the body uses glucose.

If gestational diabetes is untreated or uncontrolled, it can result in a variety of health problems for both the mother and baby. So it is important that a treatment plan is worked out to keep blood sugars within the normal range. The good news is that controlling blood sugars can help to ensure a healthy pregnancy and a healthy baby.

Latent autoimmune diabetes [LADA]

Sometimes people don't really know whether they have Type 1 or Type 2 diabetes and no one has actually told them! It could be that they have latent autoimmune diabetes [LADA] which is also called Late-onset Autoimmune Diabetes of Adulthood, Slow onset Type 1 diabetes or Type 1.5 diabetes.

People with LADA are usually diagnosed at a later age than people with typical Type 1 diabetes. It is now thought that 20% of people diagnosed with Type 2 diabetes could actually have LADA.

Unlike Type 2 diabetes, people with LADA do not have insulin resistance and are not obese or overweight at diagnosis. The characteristics of LADA are:

- Adult age at diagnosis – usually over 25 years.

- People are often mistakenly thought to have non-obese Type 2 diabetes because of their age at diagnosis and the fact they initially respond to treatment with diet with or without tablets.

- Treatment with insulin gradually becomes necessary and often within months of diagnosis. Some specialists treat LADA with insulin immediately but it is not known whether this early treatment is beneficial for the remaining insulin-producing beta cells.

- They have low C-peptide levels.

- They are unlikely to have a family history of Type 2 diabetes.

Secondary diabetes

This is where diabetes is caused by some outside source. Some drugs can cause diabetes, such as steroids and some antidepressants or it can be caused by surgery, such as removal or partial removal of the pancreas.

Pre-diabetes

- Pre-diabetes is a relatively new classification and means that blood glucose levels are higher than normal but not sufficiently high to be classed as diabetes.

- Most people with pre-diabetes do not have any symptoms but if people are overweight and over 45 years old, it may be recommended that they are tested for pre-diabetes.

- Pre-diabetes increases the risk of the development of Type 2 diabetes. Type 2 diabetes can be prevented, delayed or even reversed by weight loss of 5 to 10% of the starting weight and by being physically active.

Rare forms of diabetes

There are rare forms of diabetes such as MODY and Diabetes Insipidus.

Whichever type of diabetes you have, the more you know about your condition and how to manage it, the better you will feel and the better your health will be.

Why blood glucose levels need to be controlled

Type 1 and Type 2 diabetes are different diseases in cause, effect and treatment but the same long-term complications can arise in both conditions. The risk of complications is reduced by the treatment of diabetes with insulin or tablets, diet and exercise to reduce blood glucose levels. In Type 2 diabetes early diagnosis and treatment helps to reduce the risk of complications developing.

If blood glucose levels are too high then this can lead to long-term complications in both Type 1 and Type 2 diabetes. The risk of complications is reduced by the treatment of the condition and by lifestyle changes to reduce blood glucose levels. In Type 2 diabetes, early diagnosis is also very important as this means that treatment of the condition can begin sooner rather than later.

Good control means trying to keep blood sugar levels consistently as close to normal levels as possible. In people with Type 1 diabetes this means treatment with insulin. People with Type 2 diabetes may be prescribed medications to improve the body's sensitivity to insulin and to increase the amount of insulin the body produces. Insulin and some of the medications for Type 2 diabetes can sometimes cause the opposite problem and blood sugars drop too low (hypoglycaemia or 'hypo'). It is equally important to avoid this as hypoglycaemia is a major, daily concern for many people with diabetes.

The complications of diabetes commonly affect several areas:

The eyes – diabetes can affect the blood vessels at the back of the eye (retinopathy) which can lead to visual impairment or blindness.

The heart and vascular system – diabetes makes people more susceptible to heart disease and stroke. It can also cause blood clots in the legs which may result in amputation.

The kidneys – diabetes can cause damage to the kidneys or kidney failure.

The nerves – diabetes can cause nerve damage resulting in pain, loss of sensation in the feet and ulceration of the legs which again, can lead to amputation.

A range of carbohydrate foods

Chapter 2

Carbohydrates and controlling blood glucose levels

As we have explained in Chapter 1, it is important that blood sugar levels are kept as near normal as possible, at the same time avoiding them going too low and causing hypoglycaemia.

Three important factors in the treatment of Type 1 and Type 2 diabetes

Although Type 1 and Type 2 diabetes are very different conditions, the treatment of both types of diabetes has three factors in common – medication [insulin or tablets], diet and exercise. All three are important, they all affect blood sugar levels and they all affect each other. So in both Type 1 and Type 2 diabetes there is an important relationship between medication [insulin or tablets], diet and exercise and to achieve good diabetic control we have to try to balance all three.

> Although Type 1 and Type 2 diabetes are different conditions, the treatment of both involves balancing insulin or medication, with diet and exercise. The aim is to try to achieve as near normal blood glucose levels as possible or to achieve the target blood glucose levels set by you and your diabetes team.

In this chapter we look at the effects of consuming carbohydrates because they are very important in helping to provide the energy we need for all our activities and in controlling blood glucose levels. Exercise and medication are equally important and are discussed in Chapter 5.

Understanding Carbohydrates

Carbohydrates are sugars and starches – bread, potatoes, rice, pasta, cereals and sugar. They provide the energy our bodies need for all its various activities. Energy is also supplied by fats and proteins. The portion sizes of any meal will vary from person to person, depending on lifestyle, but the following guidelines may be helpful:

Starchy carbohydrates

Most people will eat 5-10 portions of carbohydrates a day. Where possible, you should try to choose unrefined carbohydrates such as brown rice, brown pasta, wholegrain bread or wholegrain breakfast cereals as these will provide extra fibre. Any of the items below are regarded as one portion and each portion will provide around 15g carbohydrate:

- 1 medium slice of bread or toast, preferably granary or wholemeal.
- 4 tablespoons of breakfast cereal.
- 2 tablespoons of muesli.
- Half a pitta bread or chapatti.
- 2 boiled or baked potatoes, each the size of a small egg.
- 1 tablespoon of cooked rice or pasta.

Fruit and vegetables

All of us are advised to eat 5-9 portions of fruit and vegetables a day. Ideally these should be fresh or frozen but tinned fruit or vegetables can be used for convenience. These foods are mainly low in fat (apart from avocados and olives), are full of vitamins and minerals, fibre and also antioxidants, which have an important protective effect on the body. This protective effect is particularly important for people with diabetes. A single portion of fruit or vegetables is any of the items below:

- A medium apple, orange, peach, pear or other fresh fruit.
- A small banana.
- 150ml of unsweetened fruit juice.
- A handful of grapes or cherries.
- 1 tablespoon of dried fruit.
- 3 tablespoons of tinned fruit in juice.
- 3 dates or prunes.
- 2-4 tablespoons of full vegetables.
- A bowl of side salad.

Fatty and sugary foods

These are best avoided but try and limit them to 4 portions a day. The sugary carbohydrate portions all provide approximately 15g carbohydrate, which is the same as a slice of bread. Similarly, 2 teaspoons (tsp) of butter will provide around 90 calories, the same amount as 2 apples, which would be more filling. Artificial sweeteners can be used as an alternative to sugar. Low sugar drinks, jams and jellies are also good choices. A portion is:

- 1 scoop or small block ice cream.
- 1 mini chocolate bar.
- 3 tsp sugar, jam or marmalade.
- 3 boiled sweets.
- 2 tsp margarine or butter.
- 2 tsp mayonnaise.
- Small packet of crisps

What happens to the carbohydrates in someone without diabetes?

- When we eat, beta cells in the pancreas produce insulin, a hormone which controls the glucose levels in the blood. The pancreas produces the right amount of insulin for the amount of carbohydrates we have eaten and this keeps the level of glucose in the blood within the normal range. [People WITHOUT diabetes always have blood glucose levels within certain measurements – 4 to 7mmols/l0.]
- The carbohydrates are converted into glucose which then goes into the blood and is carried around in the blood stream. It is taken to all parts of the body to provide energy wherever it is needed.
- If we have eaten more carbohydrates than we need for energy at a particular time, then the excess glucose is stored in the liver as glycogen. This is used for extra physical activity, or occasions when the blood glucose levels drop unexpectedly, such as times of fear.

What happens in people with Type 1 diabetes?

- In people with Type 1 diabetes, the cells in the pancreas cannot produce insulin. When carbohydrates are eaten, no insulin is produced and so the glucose levels in the blood rise higher and higher.
- The body cannot cope with this and so the excess glucose is passed through the body into the urine. This means that people with untreated diabetes pee a lot to get rid of the excess glucose. In turn, this makes them thirsty because the body gets dehydrated. These are the classic signs of undiagnosed diabetes – thirst and peeing.
- The body becomes short of energy as a result of the glucose being excreted and the person feels tired. The body starts to burn fats to provide the necessary energy and there is weight loss. Treatment is essential at this stage and it is often an acute emergency situation.

As the body does not produce its own insulin, the treatment of Type 1 diabetes is always with insulin. In the person without diabetes, insulin is produced in response to carbohydrates eaten but in insulin-treated diabetes, the insulin is given in regular doses, so the insulin has to be balanced with the amount of food eaten and the level of activity / exercise.

What happens in people with Type 2 diabetes?

- In Type 2 diabetes, the body either does not produce enough insulin or the insulin produced cannot be used properly by the body [insulin resistance]. So when carbohydrates are eaten, the levels of glucose in the blood rise.
- As some insulin is produced, usually the blood glucose levels do not rise as high as in Type 1 diabetes and so there may be no symptoms for many years and Type 2 diabetes can remain undiagnosed.

Initially the treatment of Type 2 diabetes could be diet only or diet and tablets and if this does not keep the blood glucose levels sufficiently low, then insulin treatment may become necessary. There are different types of tablets that either stimulate the pancreas to produce more insulin or increase the body's sensitivity to insulin so that it is used more effectively.

The type and amount of carbohydrate is important for people with diabetes

Faster absorbed carbohydrates

Carbohydrate foods like sugar, sweets and cakes are easy to eat and can provide concentrated carbohydrate. Sugary foods will raise blood sugars more quickly and higher in people with diabetes and more injected insulin or medications may be necessary. Sugary carbohydrates tend not to last as long in the body so blood sugars may drop before the next meal. They also tend to make blood sugar levels peak and trough.

Slower absorbed carbohydrates

Some carbohydrates are slower acting and last longer, such as granary or seeded bread, new potatoes, porridge and lentils. These carbohydrates do not raise the blood sugars as quickly or as high after eating. They last longer and therefore tend to give more even blood glucose levels. The amount of insulin, or in non-insulin dependent Type 2 diabetes, the medication needed may be less if sugary foods are avoided and the diet is made up of slower and longer-acting carbohydrates.

The rate at which carbohydrate foods are absorbed and cause a rise in blood sugar levels, varies according to the type of food and this is called the Glycaemic Index (GI)

For people with diabetes, the slower acting carbohydrates are better because they last longer and do not give sharp rises in blood glucose levels.

Chapter 3

Understanding your medication

In order to understand the dietary requirements for living with diabetes, it is important to have an understanding of the various medications that may be used for your diabetes and what that medication does.

Type 1 diabetes

As we have said earlier, in Type 1 diabetes the body stops producing insulin and this in turn results in the blood glucose levels rising higher and higher. The body cannot cope with this and so the excess glucose is passed through the body to the urine, hence people with untreated Type 1 diabetes pass urine frequently. In turn, this makes them thirsty because the body gets dehydrated.

Glucose is derived from the carbohydrates we eat and it is needed for energy. The body becomes short of energy as a result of the glucose being excreted so the person feels tired. As a result, the body starts to burn its own fats to provide energy and there is weight loss. Treatment is essential at this stage and Type 1 diabetes is always treated with insulin.

Understanding insulin

Type 1 diabetes is usually treated with between 2 and 4 injections a day but even so this does not mimic the body's normal action of insulin being produced according to need (that is the amount of carbohydrates eaten). Therefore the amount of insulin, its peak of activity and the duration of its action have to be balanced with the amount of carbohydrates eaten and the level of activity or energy required.

There are different types of insulin:

- Rapid and short-acting insulins deal with the carbohydrates eaten at meal times.

- Intermediate and long-acting insulins work in the background all the time.

Type 2 diabetes

Again as we have said earlier, people with Type 2 diabetes either do not produce enough insulin or the body does not correctly use the insulin it does produce. So when people with Type 2 diabetes eat carbohydrates their blood glucose levels rise.

Initially many people are advised to eat a healthy diet, increase their physical activity and to lose weight, if they are overweight. This can be sufficient to bring blood sugars down to acceptable / normal limits but if this does not happen or if at a later stage blood sugars rise, then there is a range of drugs that are introduced.

Understanding drugs for Type 2 diabetes

There are three main groups of drugs and they work in different ways.

- **Biguanides (metformin / Glucophage)** – metformin reduces insulin resistance which means it improves the body's ability to use the insulin that is still being produced. It does not increase the amount of insulin the body produces so it does not cause low blood sugars (hypoglycaemia). If metformin alone does not control blood sugars, then another drug may be added from the range known as sulfonylureas.

- **Sulfonylureas (Glibenclamide, Gliclazide, Glimepiride, Glipizide, Tolbutamide)** – these drugs increase the amount of insulin the body produces. This means that they lower blood sugar levels and can cause hypoglycaemia.

- **Glitazones (Pioglitazone)** – this can also be added to the treatment regime and it works by reducing insulin resistance in fat tissues, muscles and the liver.

- **New drugs as tablets** – there are a variety of other more recently introduced drugs which work in a variety of ways and are usually given in combination with the other tablets. They all can cause hypoglycaemia, so the only drug that does NOT cause hypoglycaemia is metformin.

- **New drugs that are injected (Byetta / exenatide, Bydureon / extended release exenatide, Victoza / liraglutide)** – these are drugs for Type 2 diabetes that are injected but they should not be confused with insulin. They stimulate the body to produce insulin, they slow down the rate at which glucose passes through the gut into the bloodstream, they cause cells in the body to remove glucose from the blood and finally they act on the brain to produce the feeling of fullness that reduces appetite and therefore food intake. So they can cause weight loss.

Adding insulin

If the above medicines do not control blood sugar levels sufficiently then the doctor may prescribe insulin.

Common side effects

Insulin – hypoglycaemia (low blood sugars).
Metformin – stomach upsets.
Sulfonylureas – stomach upsets and skin reactions.
Glitazones – there is some evidence that they cause fluid retention and increase the risk of heart attacks.
Byetta, Bydureon and Victoza – different people experience different side effects but the most common is stomach upsets.

Talk to your doctor

All drugs and different types of insulin can have side effects and these can vary from person to person. If you feel that you are having side effects, then discuss this and alternative treatments with your doctor.

Chapter 4

Hypoglycaemia – treatment and prevention

What is hypoglycaemia?

People with Type 1 and Type 2 diabetes are advised to keep their blood glucose levels as near to the normal blood glucose levels as possible, that is between 4 and 7mmols/l. If the blood glucose levels drop below normal, whatever the cause, then this is called hypoglycaemia (often referred to as a hypo).

However, having diabetes means that blood glucose levels can be too high [hyperglycaemia] or too low [hypoglycaemia].

In this chapter, we look at hypoglycaemia because for many people, especially those taking insulin, hypoglycaemia and the avoidance of it is one of their major daily concerns. People with Type 1 diabetes and those with Type 2 diabetes treated with some medications and/or insulin are at risk of low blood sugars (hypoglycaemia). Hypoglycaemia is caused by insulin or medications and not by diabetes itself.

Definitions of hypoglycaemia

Normal blood glucose levels in non-diabetic people range between 4 and 7mmols/l. Hypoglycaemia is usually said to occur at 3.9 mmols/l and so the recommended lower level is 4mmols/l – hence the recommendation to people with diabetes that '4 is the Floor' and for drivers 'drive at 5'.

Mild: a hypo that is easily treated by the patient by the intake of a sugary drink or food, often referred to as 'being low'.

Moderate: one where someone else, spouse, friend or parent, has to intervene and give the sugary food/drink because the person with diabetes is confused or even losing consciousness

Severe: one that usually means unconsciousness and maybe accompanied by a convulsion/seizure. Severe hypos rarely occur in people with Type 2 diabetes.

The causes of hypoglycaemia

The simplistic explanation of hypoglycaemia is that it is an insufficiency of carbohydrates for the exercise taken or the energy used. Some of the common causes are:

- Missing or postponing a meal or eating less than the correct allowance of carbohydrate.

- Taking more exercise than usual.

- Injecting the wrong dose of insulin (in people with insulin-treated diabetes).

- The risk of severe hypoglycaemia is increased threefold with tight control of blood glucose levels, which is keeping blood glucose at near normal levels.

- Emotional upset or stress.

- Alcohol consumption.

- No apparent reason.

Prevention of hypoglycaemia

It is not always possible to avoid all episodes of hypoglycaemia but keeping blood sugars consistently level with the avoidance of erratic blood sugars, those that dip and peak, is one of the best ways of trying to avoid hypos. In addition, eating slow-acting carbohydrates that are digested more slowly, also helps to keep blood sugars more level.

This sample menu shows you how easy it is to include slow acting carbohydrates

Breakfast
Glass of apple juice
Bowl of porridge topped with
sliced banana or other fruit
Cup of coffee with semi-skimmed milk

Mid-morning
2 oat biscuits
Cup of tea with semi-skimmed milk

Lunch
Bowl of Lentil soup
Granary roll
Plain low fat Greek yoghurt
Handful of strawberries
Cup of coffee with semi-skimmed milk

Mid afternoon
Small bag of nuts and raisins
Glass of sugar free squash

Dinner
Oven baked sausages
Roasted vegetables – including onions,
peppers, mushrooms and sweet potatoes
Broccoli steamed
Tomato sauce
Rhubarb Crumble with extra oats
Low fat and sugar-reduced custard
Cup of coffee with semi-skimmed milk

Supper
Glass low fat malted milk
Slice of granary toast with low fat spread

Treatment of hypoglycaemia

- Hypoglycaemia in its early stages (mild hypo) is treated with a sugary drink or sugary food. This should then be followed with some longer-acting carbohydrate to prevent another hypo.

- If the hypo is not treated at the above stage then there may be confusion, behavioural changes, helplessness and an inability to function properly (a moderate hypo).

- If not treated at the above stage with glucose or GlucoGel then coma occurs and this may or may not be accompanied by seizures (severe hypo).

Note

GlucoGel for a moderate hypo is a sugary gel that can be squeezed into the mouth around the cheeks and gums. It MUST NOT be given if the person is unconscious or unable to swallow because they could choke. It is available on a doctor's prescription in the UK.

Driving and hypoglycaemia

It is very important to ensure that hypoglycaemia does not occur when driving as this can be dangerous for both the driver and importantly, others on the road. The DVLA regulations introduced in 2012 state that people using insulin should test their blood glucose levels before driving and every two hours on long journeys. This is also sensible advice for people with Type 2 diabetes who are using tablets which can cause hypoglycaemia.

In case blood sugars start to drop, it is advisable to always carry snacks in the car that are easily accessible, not in the glove compartment! There is more information about snacks in Chapter 10.

Chapter 5

Physical activity and exercise

Physical activity and exercise are important for everyone but especially important for people with both Type 1 and Type 2 diabetes. Here are just some of the reasons:

- Physical activity reduces the risk of having a stroke and coronary heart disease.

- It lowers blood pressure or can prevent it developing.

- It helps to reduce weight and maintain a healthy weight.

- It raises 'good' cholesterol levels.

- It can help to relieve stress, make you feel better and it can be enjoyable.

- There is no level of activity that has to be achieved to gain health benefits.

- The largest gain in health benefits from increasing physical activity levels is in people who are inactive and who start to take regular exercise or physical activity such as walking, cycling, dancing or swimming.

However, physical activity does not have to be vigorous – evidence suggests that brisk walking for 30 minutes everyday or several times a week is effective.

It is important to eat sufficient carbohydrates before, during and after exercise or more physical activity than usual, to avoid hypoglycaemia for those treated with insulin or tablets that carry the risk of low blood sugars, by:

- Eating a meal of slow-acting carbohydrates about an hour before exercising will keep your blood sugars steady during exercise. Examples: porridge, cereal or multi-grain bread.

- Eating fast-acting carbohydrate immediately after exercise will help to prevent hypoglycaemia. It will also help to re-stock the liver stores of glycogen which the body turns into glucose when needed. Examples: a piece of fruit, fruit juice or biscuits.

- Regular blood glucose monitoring is important when exercising to avoid both high and low blood sugars.

Here are some examples of snacks

- Bananas, kiwi fruits, oranges, pears, apples, plums, strawberries
- Oat biscuits, fig rolls, garibaldi biscuits, malt loaf, low fat and sugar reduced yoghurt
- Cashew nuts, peanuts, corn chips, pot of low fat custard
- Sandwiches or toast made with oat or grainy bread
- Pasta salad
- Cup of vegetable soup
- Wholegrain breakfast cereal and semi-skimmed milk

Chapter 6

Sick days –
guidance for type 1 and type 2 diabetes

It is important for everyone with diabetes to have a 'sick-day plan' because all illnesses can affect blood glucose levels and it is important to know what to do before it happens. Your doctor or nurse can draw up a sick-day plan with you for you, your child with diabetes or the person with diabetes that you care for. This will help you:

- to know what blood glucose levels to aim for when you are sick,
- if you take insulin, to know how to adjust your insulin dose and timing, or what to do about your medications if you have Type 2 diabetes, assuming you have access to testing your blood sugars,
- to know how often to test your blood sugars and to test your urine for ketones,
- to know when to call a doctor.

You should keep your plan in a convenient place. If possible, other members of the family should know where it is and it should include contact details for your doctor and/or your diabetes nurse, day and night times.

Why is a sick-day plan is important?

Any illness, such as a cold, 'flu or an infection can upset diabetes control and usually blood glucose levels rise, even a minor illness can cause them to rise dangerously high. With illness the body reacts by releasing hormones to fight the infection but these hormones raise blood glucose levels at the same time. This can lead to diabetic ketoacidosis [DKA].

DKA is a serious complication of diabetes caused by a lack of insulin in the body. It usually occurs in people with Type 1 diabetes but it can occur as a complication of Type 2 diabetes, usually triggered by severe illness. The lack of insulin means that the body cannot break down glucose so the blood glucose levels rise very high. As the body cannot obtain energy from glucose, it breaks down fat to provide energy. During this process, ketones are produced and these cause breath to smell of pear drops or a fruity smell.

It is therefore considered important for people with Type 1 and Type 2 diabetes to continue to take their insulin and/or tablets. (Metformin is usually stopped if there is a significant risk of dehydration eg with vomiting and diarrhoea.)

General guidelines to take during illness

- If you are treated with insulin and/or tablets, you should continue to take your insulin and tablets even if you are vomiting and having trouble eating or drinking as your blood sugar may continue to rise because of the illness. If you cannot eat or drink, then call your doctor and discuss whether you need to adjust your insulin or your tablets.

- Try to eat the foods you normally eat as part of your diet and to drink extra fluids to prevent dehydration such as water or carbonated drinks – a minimum of 200mls of sugar-free fluid every hour. Comfort foods are easy to eat and may be appealing. Foods like porridge, soups, shepherds pie, mashed potatoes, fish or eggs in various ways may be tempting if you feel ill. You could also try foods that are gentle on the stomach such as crackers, apple sauce or custard. It is advisable and often easier to take food gradually throughout the day rather than the whole amount at once, so meals and snacks should be replaced with 10gms of carbohydrate every 1 to 2 hours. There are some options to try on p.33.

10gm carbohydrate 1–2 hourly meal replacements

- Lucozade or similar glucose drink – 50ml/2fl oz
- Fruit juices [natural, unsweetened] – 1 small glass 100ml/4fl oz
- Coke or Pepsi [ordinary varieties] – 1 small glass 100/4fl oz
- Lemonade or similar [sugary] fizzy drink – 1 medium glass 150ml/6fl oz
- Milk – 1 large cup 200ml/8fl oz
- Soup [thickened] –1 large cup 200ml/8 floz
  See page 59
- Drinking chocolate or malted milk drinks – 2 heaped teaspoons made up with milk
- Milk pudding – 1 bowl
  See page 88

- Natural yogurt – 1 pot 150g/5fl oz or ordinary fruit yogurt, 1/2 pot 75g/2.5fl oz
- Plain ice Cream – 1 scoop
- Sugar or glucose power – 2 teaspoons
- 3 glucose tablets

- Check your blood sugars at least every 3 to 4 hours and more often if it is rising quickly, even through the night. If you are taking insulin and your doctor or nurse has told you how much extra to take in these circumstances, then take the appropriate amount, but if you have not been told, then check with your doctor or nurse first. The aim is to bring blood glucose levels down to between 4–10 mmol/l.

- If you take insulin, test your urine for ketones every 4 hours, especially if your blood sugars are around 16mmols/l or above. Ketones are produced during diabetic ketoacidosis [DKA]. Call a doctor if you have more than 2+ or moderate ketones in your urine. In children, ketones should be checked every 4 hours, even during the night. The aim is to bring urinary ketones down to 'small, a trace, or negative'. Your GP can prescribe Ketostix to test for ketones.

- If you have a temperature and your breathing rate and pulse are increasing, contact a doctor.

- Do not take non-prescription drugs without talking to your doctor as they can affect your blood sugar levels.

When to call a doctor

If you are at all uncertain,
then you must ring your on call
Diabetes Specialist Nurse or GP.

Chapter 7

Recipes for everyday

Very often, particularly just after diagnosis, people feel confused about the advice they are given on healthy eating. They may feel insecure about what they are eating and how this may affect their diabetes or they simply do not have enough information about diet. These feelings may hold equally true for family members who will also have a role in the changes to diet that the household may have to make.

In this Chapter, we hope to give you some ideas for everyday meals that give you calorie content, as well as the amount of fat, salt and carbohydrate in each meal. There are also ideas for vegetarian and gluten-free meals and recipes for some great innovative ideas which may be useful to try for a change.

The Eatwell Plate

The usual official guidance is to eat a balanced diet by following the Eatwell Plate. You can use this to help you get the balance right. It shows the recommendations for how much of what you eat should come from each food group and includes everything you eat during the day, including snacks.

Public Health England in association with the Welsh Government, the Scottish Government and the Food Standards Agency in Northern Ireland

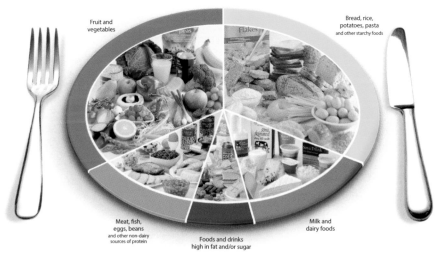

Public Health England in association with the Welsh Government, the Scottish Government and the Food Standards Agency in Northern Ireland

The trend towards lower carbohydrate intake

The usual official recommendations of the Eatwell Plate and the advice that people with diabetes should eat starchy foods with every meal, has softened over recent years. There has been a realisation that Type 1 and Type 2 diabetes are essentially conditions where there is intolerance to glucose, and so treatment with a diet containing high doses of glucose, as happens in the often recommended high carbohydrate diet, may well be counter productive and raise blood sugar levels. In turn, this makes control of blood glucose levels more difficult.

Reducing and keeping the amount of carbohydrate eaten constant also has the advantage of reducing medication and insulin daily dose. This can reduce the weight gain which happens with insulin and some medication.

There are five basic food groups

Carbohydrates which give you energy, as discussed in depth in Chapter 2. Eating carbohydrates directly affects the amount of glucose in the blood.

Fibre (roughage) helps your body to digest food. It is found in various foods including cereals, bread, fruit and vegetables.

Proteins help children's bodies to grow and adult bodies to repair themselves. They are found in foods such as meat, poultry, fish, dairy products, eggs and beans.

Fats provide energy. They are found in foods such as full fat dairy products and items containing cooking oil, butter and spreads. Nowadays red meat is not usually high in fat as it tends to be lean and only contains 5% fat. Some ready meals, cakes and pastries also often contain fats.

Vitamins and minerals are needed to keep your body healthy. They are found in a variety of foods. For example, vitamin C is found in citrus fruits and calcium is a mineral found in milk.

Important points to remember

- **Eat three meals a day** at regular times. It will help you to keep your blood sugar levels in the correct range and help you to avoid highs and lows.

- **Don't be tempted to skip breakfast** as breakfast helps to kick-start your metabolism and will make you feel more alert.

- **Drink at least 2 litres of fluid a day** as fluid is essential for all body functions. Fluids can come from a variety of sources, including tea and coffee but alcoholic and heavily caffeinated drinks don't count towards your 2 litres a day.

- **Avoid extra fat** as cutting down on fat can help with weight loss and reduce cholesterol levels and reduce the risk of heart disease. Try to grill, bake, dry roast, dry fat fry, microwave, braise and casserole your food.

- **Avoid adding extra sugar to items like drinks and cereals.** Artificial sweeteners or low calorie sweeteners can be used if required.

- **Avoid adding extra salt to food** as this can lead to raised blood pressure.

It is important to enjoy your food.

If you eat food that you don't like, then you will find it difficult to sustain a regular eating pattern. Similarly, it is also important to choose a way of eating that suits you and helps you to manage your diabetes. Often when people try to adopt a diet they don't like, they will give up out of frustration – so eat healthily but eat foods that you like and allow yourself the occasional treat.

Here is a selection of recipes. The recipes are all about inspiration for foods and perhaps different dishes to try so that you vary foods in your diet. If the recipe is not in keeping with the one you normally use, perhaps just try and adjust it so that you work toward a better balance of ingredients, like reducing the sugar, fat and salt.

Many of the recipes are easy to cook and the sort of thing that can be rustled up from the store cupboard. Often the recipes use easily obtained items like ready-made pizza bases or filo pastry. They are also mainly quite economical to make with an eye on feeding a family.

Notes for the recipes

- All the calculations are per portion without serving suggestions.

- Sweeteners are often used instead of sugar. There are various sweeteners available in different forms. Please check that the sweeteners that you use are suitable for the recipe.

- NGCI stands for 'no gluten containing ingredients'.

- V stands for 'vegetarian'.

Baked beans on granary toast

Kedgeree - serves 4, NGCI

250g smoked haddock
300ml low fat coconut milk
125g brown lentils
1 teaspoon vegetable oil
Small onion finely diced
125g mushrooms thinly sliced
1 teaspoon curry or tandoori paste (check it is NGCI)
175g cooked brown basmati rice
2 chopped hard boiled eggs

Poach the haddock in the coconut milk for about 10 minutes or until soft. Flake the haddock removing any skin and bones. Keep the milk. At the same time boil the lentils for about 15 minutes or until soft. Meanwhile, heat the oil, add the chopped onions and sliced mushrooms and cook until soft – about 4 minutes. Add the curry paste. Then add the rice and drained lentils and allow to warm through, adding some of the coconut milk to moisten the mixture. Add the flaked haddock and chopped eggs. Serve.

Typical nutritional content per serving kcals 344, carbohydrate 31g, fat 13g, saturated fat 1.3g, salt 1.4g

Comments: This is quite a substantial recipe – ideal as a breakfast before a day out walking or for brunch. It can be varied by using chickpeas instead of the fish and more curry paste.

Special beans on toast - serves one, V

Slice of granary or seeded bread
Small can baked beans
Yeast extract or BBQ sauce

Make the toast. Heat the baked beans – very quick in a microwave. Spread the toast with yeast extract or BBQ sauce and pile the beans on top.

Typical nutritional content per serving kcals 250, carbohydrate 43g, fat 2g, saturated fat 0.4g, salt 3.5g

Comments: Try different types of bread such as sour dough, oatmeal, seeded or soy and linseed. Also look for reduced sugar and reduced salt beans.

Berry Delicious - serves one, V and NGCI

150g natural yoghurt (check it is NGCI)
50g raspberries

Pile the yoghurt and raspberries into a bowl and enjoy.

Typical nutritional content per serving kcals 96, carbohydrate 13g, fat 2g, saturated fat 1.0g, salt 0.2g

Comments: Frozen raspberries are easy to keep in the freezer, just defrost the night before. Other fruit like strawberries, canned or fresh gooseberries or rhubarb are also good.

Omelette - serves one, V and NGCI

2 medium eggs
4 button mushrooms thinly sliced
1 small onion finely chopped
1 teaspoon oil

Cook the onions and mushrooms in a non-stick pan with the oil until soft, then put aside to keep warm. Beat the eggs and put in the pan to make an omelette. When firm fill with the onions and mushrooms and fold over and serve.

Typical nutritional content per serving kcals 241, carbohydrate 5g, fat 18g, saturated fat 4.2g, salt 0.4g

Comments: This is a filling breakfast with little carbohydrate. It also makes a good lunch. The vegetables can be varied and you can use courgettes, roasted peppers or if in season, asparagus lightly cooked. The vegetables can be added to the omelette mixture with a sprinkle of grated parmesan rather than filling the omelette.

Berry delicious

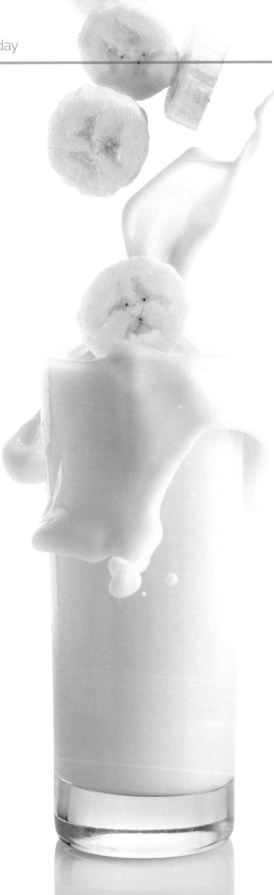

Breakfast Shake
- serves one, V and NGCI

150 ml skimmed milk
1 medium banana
Put the milk and banana together in a
liquidiser and whizz up.

Typical nutritional content per serving
kcals 143, carbohydrate 28g, fat 1g,
saturated fat 0.3g, salt 0.2g

Comments: this is a really quick and easy
breakfast to drink on the go. It is easily
adapted with other fruits like mangoes.

1 Pizza - serves one
**(This could be vegetarian if the pizza base
and cheese are checked for V)**

Small 17cm thin pizza base
2 tablespoons tomato pizza topping
25g low fat cheese
1 medium onion sliced into thin rings
4 mushrooms sliced

Spread the tomato topping on the pizza, pile on the vegetables, sprinkle on the cheese and bake until the cheese is melted.

Typical nutritional content per serving kcals 412, carbohydrate 63g, fat 9g, saturated fat 2.5g, salt 1.3g

Comments: This is a simple lunchtime snack or can be scaled up for a family meal. Vary the toppings with pineapple and chicken.

Paté - serves 4, NGCI

200g lambs liver chopped
100g finely chopped streaky bacon
1 small finely chopped onion
1 clove of garlic (optional)
2 teaspoons chopped thyme
2 teaspoons chopped parsley
Quarter teaspoon cayenne pepper
Seasoning as required
4 slices granary toast – use gluten
free bread for NGCI version

In a non-stick pan cook the bacon until golden brown and the fat comes away from the bacon. Add the chopped onion and cook until soft. Add the liver and rest of the ingredients and cook for about 2 minutes or until the liver is brown. Allow the mix to cool slightly then blend to a coarse or smooth consistency, whichever you prefer. Allow to cool and transfer to individual ramekin dishes. Serve on granary toast.

Typical nutritional content per serving kcals 237, carbohydrate 18g, fat 10g, saturated fat 3.1g, salt 1.4g

Comments: This is such an easy paté to make and retains all of the goodness of liver. It can be varied with using all types of liver including chicken liver. For a starter for dinner parties, it can be enlivened with a couple of tablespoons of brandy or cranberry juice and decorated with berries, fresh bay leaves or other herbs. It is also nice piled into large mushrooms.

Note: Liver is not recommended for pregnant women.

Bean salad - serves 4, NGCI

400g red kidney beans drained and rinsed
400g chickpeas drained and rinsed
400g bartoli beans drained and rinsed
2 tablespoons balsamic vinegar (check it is NGCI)
1 tablespoon lemon juice

Mix all the beans together and toss in the vinegar and lemon juice so the beans are coated. Serve with a green salad.

Typical nutritional content per serving kcals 125, carbohydrate 18g, fat 2g, saturated fat 0.2g, salt 0.7g

Comments: This is such an easy recipe and can be varied with different beans or by adding sweet corn.

Ham, cheese and lettuce sandwiches - serves one

2 slices seeded bread
1 thin slice ham
1 thin slice strong cheddar cheese
1 teaspoon mango chutney or low fat spread
2 lettuce leaves
1 sliced small tomato

Spread the mango chutney or low fat spread on the bread and fill the sandwich with the lettuce, tomato ham and cheese.

Typical nutritional content per serving kcals 400, carbohydrate 40g, fat 17g, saturated fat 9.5g, salt 2.8g.

Comments: This is such an easy sandwich to make and can be varied with the cheese being replaced with cottage cheese and yeast extract.

Cabbage soup - serves 6, V and NGCI

1 tablespoon rapeseed oil
1 medium onion finely chopped
1 garlic clove – optional
Fresh bay leaf
4 tablespoons parsley
1 tablespoon oregano
400g tin chopped tomatoes
400g tin butter beans drained and rinsed
450g cabbage, finely chopped
700ml water
2 vegetable stock cubes
(check they are NGCI)
Pepper to taste

Fry the onion in the oil in a large sauce pan until soft and clear. Add the herbs and tomatoes and cook for 10 minutes. Add the rest of ingredients except the cabbage and bring to the boil. Simmer for 30 minutes. Add the cabbage and cook for a further 10 minutes. Season to taste and serve.

Typical nutritional content per serving kcals 70, carbohydrate 7g, fat 3g, saturated fat 0.4g, salt 1.0g

Comments: It is easy to vary the vegetables in soup.

Poached salmon with ginger - serves 4, NGCI

4 salmon steaks about 125g each
5 spring onions chopped into lengths
2 cm ginger root peeled and cut into batons
4 tablespoons low calorie ginger mixer drink

Mix the ginger drink, onions and ginger together. Put the mixture into a covered pan, add the salmon steaks and poach each side for 5 minutes. If the liquid boils off, add low calorie ginger mixer drink. Serve with salad or steamed cabbage and new potatoes.

Typical nutritional content per serving kcals 232, carbohydrate 1g, fat 14g, saturated fat 2.4g, salt 0.1g

Comments: Salmon provides omega 3 fatty acids as well as vitamin D. It can be poached with various items like diluted soya sauce.

Turkey burgers - serves 4

250g turkey mince
1 small onion finely chopped
1 egg beaten
1 teaspoon soya sauce or Worcester sauce
50g wholemeal breadcrumbs
50g porridge oats

Mix everything in a bowl, cover and leave in the fridge for 30-60 minutes so that the oats and breadcrumbs absorb the moisture. Divide into 4 burgers and shape with clean hands. Pre-heat a grill to medium and grill for 8 minutes each side or until thoroughly cooked so no pink is visible.

Typical nutritional content per serving kcals 188, carbohydrate 19g, fat 4g, saturated fat 0.8g, salt 0.3g

Comments: You can vary this by including tomato sauce or chilli sauce in the mix. Grated carrots can be added. It works well with other types of lean mince or indeed lentils, chick peas and red kidney beans all cooked or from cans and well drained.

Quick and easy spaghetti bolognese

Quick and easy spaghetti bolognese - serves 4

300g lean beef mince
Jar of ready-made tomato pasta sauce
50g mushrooms sliced
1 medium onion chopped
Oregano or basil (optional)
200g spaghetti or shorter pasta shapes if you prefer

Dry fry the mince in a non stick saucepan until cooked. Add the onions and mushrooms and cook until soft. Add the jar of pasta sauce plus herbs and cook as directed on the jar. Meanwhile cook the spaghetti in boiling water.

Typical nutritional content per serving kcals 342, carbohydrate 45g, fat 6g, saturated fat 1.7g, salt 1.4g.

Comments: You can make your own sauce with canned tomatoes and add extra items like garlic.

Sausage mixed grill - serves one

2 low fat sausages
2 large mushrooms
2 medium tomatoes cut in half

Grill all of the ingredients until the sausages are well cooked and not pink inside and the mushrooms and tomatoes soft. Serve with a BBQ sauces, salsa or chutney.

Typical nutritional content per serving kcals 214, carbohydrate 13g, fat 11g, saturated fat 3.9g, salt 2.2g

Comments: You can use also vegetarian sausages. This makes a good dish on the BBQ. To ensure that the sausages are cooked on the inside, it is helpful to first cook them for 2-3 minutes in the microwave.

Chicken stir fry - serves 4, NGCI

1 tablespoon sesame oil
250g chicken breast
100g broccoli
1 small onion
100g carrots
100g bean sprouts
50g shitake mushrooms or use
ordinary ones
1 tablespoon soy sauce or you can
use one of the ready prepared stir fry
mixes in a packet, jar or tube (check it
is NGCI)

Chop the onion finely, cut the carrots into batons, finely slice the onions, slice the broccoli and the mushrooms. Heat the oil and cook the chicken and onions for 5 minutes. Add the broccoli and carrots and stir fry for a further 5 minutes until soft. Add the mushrooms and cook for 1-2 minutes. Add the soy sauce or bought stir fry mix and cook for a minute – stirring thoroughly. Serve immediately.

Typical nutritional content per serving kcals 134, carbohydrate 5g, fat 5g, saturated fat 0.8g, salt 0.1g

Comments: You can vary this by using strips of pork, beef or any vegetables.

Marmalade bread pudding - serves 6 V

    600ml skimmed milk
    3 eggs
    Sweetener
    6 slices wholemeal bread
    6 heaped teaspoons of marmalade
    Zest of orange or orange peel

Whisk the eggs, milk and sweetener together. Spread the sliced bread with marmalade and place in a dish. As you finish a layer pour the egg mixture over it. Continue until you fill the dish. Top with orange zest or peel. Bake in an oven pre-heated to 160°C, gas mark 3 for 30 minutes until set.

Typical nutritional content per serving kcals 220, carbohydrate 35g, fat 4g, saturated fat 1.2g, salt 0.7g

Comment: You can leave out the marmalade. You can use sultanas or low fat spread to make a more traditional pudding.

Fruit crumble - serves 4

450g rhubarb, apple, plums or mixture or any other fruit
Sweetener to taste
2 tablespoons granulated sugar
100g plain flour – it will still work if you use self raising flour – you can add 25g of wholemeal flour and use less white flour if you prefer
50g low fat spread
50g (2 tablespoons) rolled oats – jumbo ones are nice but the cheap and cheerful porridge oats are fine

Pre-heat the oven to 180C/350F gas mark 4. Place the fruit and sweetener in a pan with 4 tablespoons of water and cover and simmer for 10 minutes until the fruit is tender. Transfer to an ovenproof dish. Meanwhile, with your fingertips, rub together the flour, low fat spread and sugar, (you cannot easily use a sweetener for this) stir through the oats, then sprinkle over the fruit. Bake for 25-30 minutes until golden and bubbling.

Typical nutritional content per serving kcals 233, carbohydrate 45g, fat 4g, saturated fat 0.5g, salt 0.2g

Comments: If you use rhubarb, a pinch of ginger goes well or if you use apple, cinnamon is lovely. For variations you can add a spoonful of desiccated coconut, mixed seeds or chopped nuts to the crumble mix. In doing this at home I never use sugar in the fruit and just rub the flour and fat into a breadcrumb texture, stir through the oats and then sprinkle with sugar before putting in the oven. It can be served with plenty of custard which may offset the lack of sweetness.

Creamy orange jelly - serves 4

Packet of sugar free orange jelly
300 ml skimmed milk
2 mandarin oranges divided into segments

Make up the jelly according to the instructions but use milk instead of part of the water. Allow to set. Serve decorated with mandarin segments.

Typical nutritional content per serving kcals 52, carbohydrate 8g, fat 0g, saturated fat 0g, salt 0.2g

Comment: This is such an easy dessert and can be made with different fruits and jellies.

Pancakes with fruit - serves 4

50g flour - half plain and half wholemeal
2 eggs beaten
75ml skimmed milk
1 tablespoon vegetable oil
100g apple puree with pinch of cinnamon, warmed

Sift the flour, add the milk and eggs to make a batter which should be the consistency of single cream. Cover and allow to stand in the fridge. Heat the oil in a small non-stick frying pan. Pour in a small amount of mixture and run evenly round the pan. When cooked toss or turn with a spatula. Place on a plate and top with the apple and cinnamon. Serve.

Typical nutritional content per serving kcals 132, carbohydrate 11g, fat 7g, saturated fat 1.4g, salt 0.1g

Comment: You can use other fruits as an alternative.

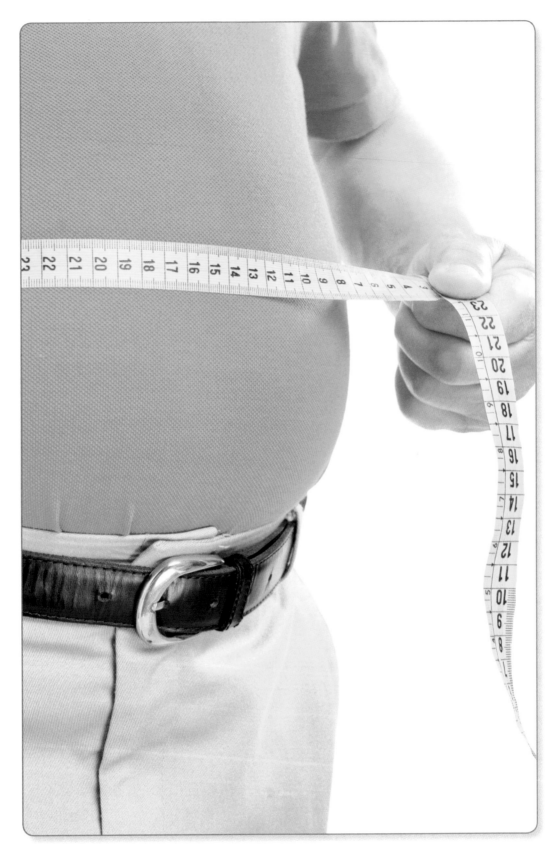

Chapter 8

Recipes for weight loss

Many people with Type 2 diabetes are overweight when they are diagnosed and so one of the first things they are advised to do is to lose weight. There are several reasons for this and just a 10% reduction in your body weight will increase the likelihood that:

- Your blood sugar levels will drop and you are likely to need less or no medication as a result.

- Your blood pressure will reduce.

- Your cholesterol levels will fall.

The following principles apply to people with both Type 1 and Type 2 diabetes who want or need to lose weight.

If you eat fewer calories than you use up, then you will lose weight. On average a woman needs 2000 calories a day and a man, 2500 calories a day. If you reduce your calorie intake by 500 calories a day, then you should lose around half a kilo (about a pound) a week. If you take extra exercise, such as walking, gardening or swimming, then you should use up more calories and lose more weight.

The recipes in this section all aim to be below 500kcal per main course and 200kcal per pudding – that leaves enough calories for accompaniments like potatoes and vegetables and also milk for drinks and between meal snacks.

Note: these recipes are good for anyone not just those wanting to lose weight

In reality losing weight is not easy and keeping weight off is harder still. There are several things you can do to help you lose weight and these involve simple lifestyle changes. It is a good idea to make these changes gradually at your own pace so that you can feel you have mastered each change before moving on to the next one.

Tips for changing your eating habits to help you to lose weight

- Eat more slowly to make the meal last
- Use a smaller plate – it makes it look as if you have more food
- Fill your plate with vegetables or salad
- Don't feel you have to clear your plate – stop eating when you have had enough
- Try to cook tasty low-calorie foods that the rest of the family will enjoy so that you don't feel left out
- Set realistic targets for losing weight – don't set yourself up to fail by being over ambitious
- Be wary of hidden calories in salad dressings and sauces
- Make a shopping list before going to the supermarket and stick strictly to the list and don't go shopping for food when you are hungry
- Avoid alcohol

Grilled mushrooms on toast

Breakfasts

Perfect porridge - serves one, V

3 tablespoons porridge oats
200ml skimmed milk

Mix the oats and water or milk in a bowl and pop in the microwave for 2 minutes. Stir and add more water if needed. Return to the microwave for a minute. Serve topped with blackberries and apple slices.

Typical nutritional content per serving kcals 244, carbohydrate 39g, fat 4.3g, saturated fat 0.3g, salt 0.3g

Comment: You can use water to make the porridge. You can also top up with apple slices and berries.

Grilled mushrooms on toast - serves 2, V

2 large open mushrooms
2 slices of toasted granary or wholemeal bread
Grill the mushrooms and serve on the 2 slices of the toasted bread

Typical nutritional content per serving kcals 93, carbohydrate 17g, fat 1g, saturated fat 0.2g, salt 0.5g

Comment: You can use different types of bread. You can also use tomatoes instead of mushrooms.

Boiled egg and soldiers - serves one, V

One egg
1 slice granary bread

Boil the egg so it is still soft and serve with the toasted granary bread as soldiers.

Typical nutritional content per serving kcals 177, carbohydrate 17g, fat 7g, saturated fat 2.0g, salt 0.7g

Comment: You can boil the egg to taste so that it is soft or hard.

Seeded toast - serves one, V

2 slices granary or wholemeal bread
2 teaspoons peanut butter
2 teaspoons of pumpkin seeds

Toast the bread, spread with peanut butter and top with the seeds.

Typical nutritional content per serving kcals 408, carbohydrate 38g, fat 21g, saturated fat 5.0g, salt 1.3g

Comment: You can use different seeds.

Bacon 'Sarnies' - serves one

2 slices granary bread
2 slices lean back bacon
1 tomato sliced

Grill the bacon and serve in the bread with the tomato as a sandwich.

Typical nutritional content per serving kcals 332, carbohydrate 36g, fat 13g, saturated fat 4.5g, salt 3.5g

Comment: You can use gluten free bread.

Lunches and light meals

Lentil and tomato soup - serves 4, V and NGCI

50g dried split lentils
2 vegetable stock cubes (check
they are NGCI)
500ml boiling water
1 large onion chopped
400g can chopped tomatoes
1 teaspoon mixed herbs

Dissolve the stock cubes in the boiling
water. Add the lentils and simmer
for 15 minutes. Add the rest of the
ingredients and simmer for at least 30
minutes until everything is soft. You
can use a blender to make it smooth.

Typical nutritional content per serving kcals 88, carbohydrate 14g, fat 1g, saturated fat 0g,
salt 1.6g

Comment: You can use any vegetables.

Pork and pesto salad - serves one

Handful of salad leaves
50g cooked lean pork cut into small pieces
50g cooked macaroni or small shaped pasta
5 cherry tomatoes
Dessertspoonful red pesto

Mix all of the ingredients together in a bowl.

Typical nutritional content per serving kcals 272, carbohydrate 11g, fat 16g, saturated fat
1.3g, salt 0.3g

Comment: Try other salad leaves like chard or spinach. You can use strips of chicken or beef
instead of pork.

Potato cakes - serves 4, V

250g mashed potatoes
200g sweetcorn drained
3 tablespoons oat bran
1 egg beaten lightly
1 tablespoon vegetable oil

Mix the potato, 2 tablespoons bran, sweet corn and eggs together. Divide into 4 parts and pat into flat rounds toss in the remaining oat bran. Fry in the oil for approximately 3 minutes each side.

Typical nutritional content per serving kcals 234, carbohydrate 30g, fat 9g, saturated fat 1.8g, salt 0.6g

Comment: Other vegetables, such as onions, can be added to the mixture.

Wrap it up - serves 4

4 wraps or tortillas
1 teaspoon olive oil
1 small onion chopped
200g lean pork mince
Clove of garlic (optional)
1 small pepper deseeded and chopped
2 large chopped mushrooms
1 tablespoon soy sauce
1 tablespoon tomato sauce
125g bean sprouts

Fry the onions in the oil until soft, add the pork and garlic and cook for 4 minutes. Add all of the other ingredients except the bean sprouts and cook for 4 minutes stirring all the time. Add the bean sprouts and cook for another 2 minutes. Serve in warmed tortillas.

Typical nutritional content per serving kcals 250, carbohydrate 35g, fat 4g, saturated fat 1.1g, salt 0.5g

Comment: You can use other flat breads or serve the filling with a salad.

Open sandwich - serves one, V

1 slice granary or wholemeal bread
Yeast extract
100g plain cottage cheese
6 cucumber slices
1 medium tomato sliced
3 strips green pepper

Spread the bread with the yeast extract. Pile on the cottage cheese and then top with the vegetables.

Typical nutritional content per serving kcals 217, carbohydrate 23g, fat 6g, saturated fat 2.7g, salt 1.5g

Comment: You can use pickle instead of the yeast extract.

Beef casserole

Beef casserole - serves 4

450g lean braising or stewing beef
1 tablespoon oil
2 sticks celery cut into chunks
½ small swede, peeled and cut into chunks
2 carrots, peeled and cut into large chunks
2 parsnips, peeled and cut into large chunks
600ml (1pint) water
1 beef stock cube
15ml/ 1 tablespoon English mustard (optional)
30ml/ 2 tablespoons gravy granules (optional)

Brown the beef in the oil. Put into a casserole dish. Add the rest of the ingredients apart from the gravy granules. Bring to the boil. Cook for 2 hours or longer in an oven at 190°C, 170°C fan, gas mark 5. Add the gravy granules at the end to thicken and return to the oven for 5 minutes.

Typical nutritional content per portion: kcal 294, carbohydrate 14g, fat 15g, saturated fat 3.4g, salt 3.0g

Comment: This is a good warming recipe. It has mustard in it for extra flavour but if you do not like it, just leave it out or just use a pinch to see how you like it and then add more on other occasions to suit your taste.

It is also easy to cook in a slow cooker.

Liver and onions - serves 4

450g lambs liver in thin slices
2 tablespoons plain flour
1 tablespoon oil
1 large onion sliced
Beef stock cube
500ml (18fl oz) boiling water
2 tablespoons tomato ketchup

Put the flour in a bowl and coat each slice of liver in it. Fry the onions in the oil until transparent. Remove from the pan. Fry each slice of liver for 2 minutes on each side. Add the onions back to the pan with the water and stock cube and stir so that the liquid thickens with the flour. Add the tomato ketchup. Simmer for 20 minutes or until the gravy reduces and thickens.

Typical nutritional content per serving kcals 255, carbohydrate 14g, fat 11g, saturated fat 2.4g, salt 1.3g

Comment: Liver is not suitable for pregnant women due to its vitamin A content, but otherwise liver makes a nutritious and economical meal.

Shepherds pie - serves 4

2 teaspoons polyunsaturated spread
1 large onion, chopped
1 large carrot, chopped
450g minced lean lamb
100g button mushrooms chopped
400g can chopped tomatoes
Seasoning to taste
900g potatoes boiled and mashed.

Brown the lamb in a pan with the polyunsaturated spread, add the onions and mushrooms. Add the chopped carrots, tomatoes and seasoning. Bring to the boil, cover and simmer for 40 minutes. Put the mixture into an ovenproof dish or individual dishes and top with the mash. Bake in oven at 190°C, 170°C fan, gas mark 5 for 20-30 minutes.

Typical nutritional content per serving kcals 473, carbohydrate 42g, fat 21g, saturated fat 6.4g, salt 1.1g

Comment: This is a bit higher in calories but does not need to be served with extra potatoes just with vegetables. Lamb is one of the meats which contains more fat. The dish can also be made with lean beef mince.

Beef and vegetable balti - serves 4

450g lean minced beef
1 large onion sliced
1 clove garlic crushed
1-2 tbsp balti curry paste
1 red chilli (optional)
1 small cauliflower cut into small florets
400g tin chopped tomatoes
250 ml boiling water
Beef stock cube (check it is NGCI)
100g butternut squash cubed (optional)

Heat a deep non-stick pan and dry fry the beef and onions for 5 minutes until brown, stirring constantly. Add the curry paste, garlic and chilli and cook for 3 minutes, stirring constantly. Make up a stock with the boiling water and stock cube. Add the squash, cauliflower, tomatoes and stock. Bring to the boil and then simmer for 20-30 minutes, stirring occasionally.

Typical nutritional content per serving kcals 234, carbohydrate 10g, fat 8g, saturated fat 2.1g, salt 1.4g

Comment: You can use other meats in this balti or even use chick peas instead. The vegetables can be varied, however, the cauliflower does give a lovely texture.

Fish cakes - serves one

50g canned salmon drained
100g mashed potatoes
1 tablespoon breadcrumbs
1 small egg beaten
1 tablespoon oil

Mix the mashed potatoes and salmon together. Add the egg gradually to bind it together. Flatten the mix and roll in the breadcrumbs. Fry for 6 minutes each side in the oil.

Typical nutritional content per serving kcals 471, carbohydrate 29g, fat 30g, saturated fat 5.2g, salt 1.2g

Comment: Salmon is higher in fat than other fish because it contains omega 3 fatty acids. Fish such as cooked cod could be substituted for salmon.

Desserts

Fruit salad - serves 4, V and NGCI

Small tin of pineapple in natural juice
One banana sliced – slice this last or it may
discolour
Half a mango, or small yellow melon, cubed
2 golden kiwi fruits peeled and sliced

Arrange all of the ingredients together in a bowl
or individual serving glasses

Typical nutritional content per serving kcals 68,
carbohydrate 15g, fat 0g, saturated fat 0g, salt 0g

Comment: If you do not have any of the above fruit, substitute another one.

Raspberry jelly - serves 4, V and NGCI

Packet of sugar free raspberry jelly
150g raspberries fresh, or frozen and thawed
Low fat cream

Make up a sugar free jelly according to the directions on the packet. Allow to cool and add
100g of the raspberries and put in individual tall serving glasses. When cooled, place in the
fridge so the glasses are slightly slanted and the jelly sets at an angle. Add the rest of the fruit
to the glasses and serve with a blob of low fat cream.

Typical nutritional content per serving kcals 25, carbohydrate 2g, fat 1g, saturated fat 0.6g,
salt 0.1g

Comment: Vary the fruit and jellies.

Apricot pudding - serves 4, V

50g low fat spread
50g brown sugar
50g self raising flour
1 egg beaten
1 tablespoon skimmed milk
50g ready to eat dried apricots chopped.

Beat the spread and sugar until light and fluffy, add the eggs, milk and flour so a soft dropping consistency is achieved. Add the apricots and mix through. Lightly grease 4 ramekins or use 4 silicone muffin tins. Pour into the ramekins. Bake in a pre-heated oven at 180°C, gas mark 4 for 20-30 minutes until firm.

Typical nutritional content per serving kcals 179, carbohydrate 26g, fat 7g, saturated fat 1.5g, salt 0.4g

Comment: Canned pineapple in its own juice can be used instead of the apricots.

Baked apple - serves one, V and NGCI

1 medium cooking apple
1 tablespoon of mixed fruit
1 teaspoon brown sugar
Cinnamon (optional)
Half teaspoon polyunsaturated spread

Wash and core the apple but do not peel. Add the mixed fruit and top with the sugar and any remaining spread. Put the apple in a greased ovenproof dish. Bake in a pre-heated oven 180°C, gas mark 4 for 20-30 minutes until soft.

Typical nutritional content per serving kcals 133, carbohydrate 27g, fat 2g, saturated fat 0.4g, salt 0.1g

Comment: Other dried fruits, such cranberries, could be used for the filling.

Egg custard - serves 4, V and NGCI

3 eggs,
1 teaspoon vanilla extract (optional)
450ml semi skimmed milk,
Sweetener to taste
Nutmeg (optional)

Lightly beat the eggs and milk add the sweetener and vanilla. Put in an ovenproof dish and stand this in a roasting pan half filled with hot water. Sprinkle the nutmeg on top. Bake in a preheated oven 170°C, gas mark 4 for 25-30 minutes until firm.

Typical nutritional content per serving kcals 116, carbohydrate 5g, fat 7g, saturated fat 2.6g, salt 0.3g

Comment: A chocolate version can be made by using a teaspoon of cocoa powder.

Chapter 9

Recipes for special diets

Diabetes and coeliac disease

Type 1 diabetes and coeliac disease are both autoimmune diseases and there is increasing research to show that there is a link between the two in all age groups. There are views that more attention should be given to this link and that tests for coeliac disease should be routinely carried out in both adults and children with Type 1 diabetes.

What is coeliac disease?

- It is a condition in which the lining of the small intestine is damaged by gluten. Gluten is a protein found in rye, wheat, barley and possibly oats.

- This damage causes foods to not be absorbed properly by the small intestine so before diagnosis, there is weight loss and possibly malnutrition.

- Treatment is a gluten free diet.

- In the general population about 0.75% of people have coeliac disease, but it rises to 2-10% in those with Type 1 diabetes. Therefore the NICE guidelines recommend that all children and adults with Type 1 diabetes are screened for coeliac disease.

- It can be diagnosed at any age but mostly it is finally diagnosed in adulthood between the ages of 30-45.

- Many other cases may remain undiagnosed or may be falsely diagnosed as irritable bowel syndrome. Only a third of cases are ever diagnosed as coeliac disease and treated with a gluten free diet.

Coeliac disease is nearly always diagnosed by a gastroenterologist. A new test measures antibodies in the blood to gluten and gliaden in the diet. A strict gluten free diet is the only treatment to put the intestine back to normal but this strict gluten free diet has to be followed for this normal state to be maintained.

Diabetes requires a well balanced diet with plenty of carbohydrate but once coeliac disease has been diagnosed, providing carbohydrate becomes more difficult as many of the carbohydrates we eat and enjoy, such as bread, pasta, cereal, pastry, crackers, biscuits and cakes, contain gluten, which has to be avoided. These foods can be replaced with gluten-free products, some of which are available on the NHS in the UK. As there is negligible gluten in the flour, the products do not have the same consistency and taste and are often not so delicious. This is particularly difficult for children.

Here are just some of the issues:

- There is a lack of choice.
- Pre-prepared foods are much more difficult to obtain because many of them contain gluten. For example, the flour used to thicken sauces contains gluten.
- It takes time to become familiar with the 'hidden' gluten, for example, wheat flour is often used as a carrier for flavouring in such things as crisps.
- Buying gluten-free products is very expensive.

With the realisation of the sensitivity of some people to gluten and how little gluten is required to cause a problem, it was decided that only foods which contain no more than 20 parts gluten in a million parts of food can be labelled as gluten free. This legislation came into effect on 1st January 2012. Now the only foods which can be described as gluten free are:

- Specially made foods for people with gluten intolerances such as pasta made from rice instead of wheat flour.
- Everyday foods such as soup made only from vegetables which would contain less than 20 parts per million.

More detailed information on coeliac disease can be obtained from Coeliac UK, http://www.coeliac.org.uk/

Low fat diet

All the recipes are analysed to enable those following a low fat diet or low saturated fat diet to choose suitable dishes. Most people on low fat diets aim to reduce the fat level to 40-50g per day.

Salt restricted diet

Recipes also show the salt content and therefore can help those following a salt restricted diet.

Milk free diet

Recipes can easily be used by substituting soya milk for the normal cow's milk and using a milk free spread.

Vegetarian diet

Following a vegetarian diet is a lifestyle choice to eat no meat, poultry, offal, shell fish, fish or items derived from these. Milk and milk products and eggs are eaten, all of which are sources of protein. Milk also contains calcium.

As meat is a source of iron, the vegetarian diet can become low in iron unless it is correctly balanced. Pulses, nuts and seeds contain iron as well as protein, so they should be included. There are a number of vegetarian products available although some can be high in fat, so it is worth checking labels.

Vegans

People who chose to follow a vegan diet avoid all foods of animal origin, so they do not eat eggs, milk or honey as well as excluding meat, poultry, offal, shell fish, fish or items derived from these.

They need to carefully balance the diet as it can become low in vitamin B12 which is found mainly in foods of animal origin. Suitable sources of B12 for vegans are yeast extract, fortified breakfast cereals and seaweeds, so use yeast extracts in cooking and as spreads. Pulses like lentils, beans and chickpeas, nuts and seeds can be included to provide protein and iron. Vitamin C from fruit juices as well as fruit and vegetables, helps to increase the absorption of these forms of iron. Fortified soy drinks and desserts can provide calcium.

The Vegetarian Eatwell Plate

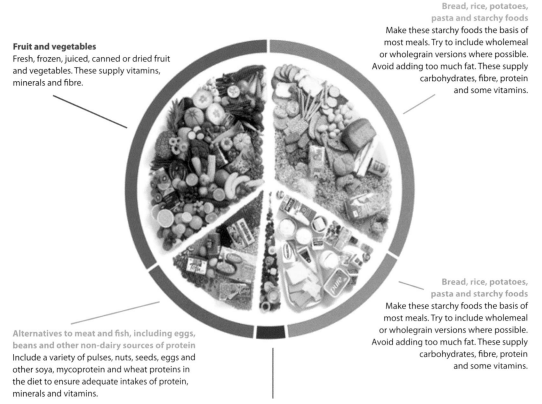

Fruit and vegetables
Fresh, frozen, juiced, canned or dried fruit and vegetables. These supply vitamins, minerals and fibre.

Bread, rice, potatoes, pasta and starchy foods
Make these starchy foods the basis of most meals. Try to include wholemeal or wholegrain versions where possible. Avoid adding too much fat. These supply carbohydrates, fibre, protein and some vitamins.

Alternatives to meat and fish, including eggs, beans and other non-dairy sources of protein
Include a variety of pulses, nuts, seeds, eggs and other soya, mycoprotein and wheat proteins in the diet to ensure adequate intakes of protein, minerals and vitamins.

Bread, rice, potatoes, pasta and starchy foods
Make these starchy foods the basis of most meals. Try to include wholemeal or wholegrain versions where possible. Avoid adding too much fat. These supply carbohydrates, fibre, protein and some vitamins.

Foods and drinks high in fat and / or sugar
Although some fat is needed in the diet, eat these foods sparingly, and look out for low fat alternatives.

- Recipes suitable for those excluding gluten are marked NGCI
- Recipes suitable for vegetarians are marked V
- It should be noted that some other recipes throughout the book are also suitable so it is important to check through ingredients.

Orange and mango smoothie - serves 4, V and NGCI

4 oranges peeled and segmented
1 mango peeled and deseeded and cut into
chunks

Put the oranges and mango into a liquidiser or
smoothie maker and whizz up.

Typical nutritional content per serving kcals 81,
carbohydrate 18g, fat 0g, saturated fat 0g, salt 0g

Comment: Other fruits can be used.

No bread steak sandwich - serves 4, NGCI

4 lean beef steaks approx 100g each
1 large onion cut into thin rings
4 teaspoons English mustard made up
2 large aubergines split long ways into 8 slices
10 ml vegetable oil

Brush or spray the aubergine slices with oil. Put under a hot grill and cook until soft. Do the same
with the onion rings and also cook until soft. Meanwhile, grill the steaks according to taste.
Make the sandwich by using the slices of aubergine instead of bread and fill with a slice of
steak and then onion rings before topping with a further slice of aubergine. Serve with the
mustard.

Typical nutritional content per serving kcals 226, carbohydrate 9g, fat 9g, saturated fat 2.3g,
salt 2g

Comment: Other steaks or burgers from different meats or poultry can be used.

Egg white omelette - serves one, V and NGCI

3 egg whites – save the yolks
1 teaspoon poly-unsaturated spread
4 button mushrooms sliced and cooked
Salt and black pepper to taste
1 teaspoon chives (optional)

Beat the egg whites with a fork and add the chives and season. Pour the mix into the heated frying pan, spread into an omelette and move the mixture around with a spatula until it cooks evenly. When cooked but still moist add the mushrooms and leave to warm through for a minute. Fold over and serve.

Typical nutritional content per serving kcals 75, carbohydrate 0g, fat 4g, saturated fat 0.9g, salt 1.1g

Comment: Save the yokes, they are nice added to the egg custard recipe or other recipes where egg yolks are required, such as homemade mayonnaise.

Carrot juice - serves one, V and NGCI

One apple peeled and cored
2 large carrots
Small piece ginger peeled – optional

Put all the ingredients into a juicer or liquidiser and whizz up until smooth.

Typical nutritional content per serving kcals 129, carbohydrate 28g, fat 1g, saturated fat 0.2g, salt 0.2g

Comment: An orange can be substituted for the apple.

Grapefruit and melon segments - serves 2, V and NGCI

One pink grapefruit segmented
One slice melon cut into chunks
Plain low fat Greek yoghurt or soya dessert (check it is NGCI)

Mix the fruit in a bowl and top with the yoghurt

Typical nutritional content per serving kcals 87, carbohydrate 14g, fat 0g, saturated fat 0g, salt 0.1g

Comment: If a white grapefruit is used instead of the melon, the carbohydrate content will be lower.

Stuffed peppers

Stuffed peppers - serves 4, V and NGCI

4 medium red peppers – tops removed to make a lid and seeds removed from bases
400g can chopped tomatoes drain off some of the liquid
1 large onion finely chopped
200g hallumi cheese chopped
100g cooked rice
1 teaspoon oregano
1 tablespoon vegetable oil

Preheat the oven to 180°C, gas mark 4. Heat the oil and cook the onions until soft. Add the tomatoes and herbs. Bring to the boil and simmer until thickened. Add the rice and the cheese and pile into the peppers. Stand the peppers in a baking tray and bake for about 25 minutes or until soft.

Typical nutritional content per serving kcals 323, carbohydrate 24g, fat 18g, saturated fat 8.6g, salt 1.4g

Comment: Other mixtures instead of cheese can be used to stuff the peppers, such as bacon for non-vegetarians.

Lentil curry - serves 4, V and NGCI

250g washed orange lentils
10 ml vegetable oil
1 large onion chopped
2 cloves garlic – optional
4 large peeled deseeded tomatoes
1 tablespoon curry paste, (check curry paste is NGCI)
600ml boiling water
Handful chopped coriander – optional

Add the lentils to the pan of water and bring to the boil. Simmer for 15 minutes or until soft. Meanwhile fry the onion until soft and add the curry paste. Drain some of the water from the lentils and add to the spicy mixture in the pan. Add the chopped tomatoes and continue to cook for a further 10-15 minutes to incorporate the flavours. The lentils should be soft and mixture smooth but not sloppy, if it is too thick add more hot water.

Typical nutritional content per serving kcals 279, carbohydrate 41g, fat 5g, saturated fat 0.5g, salt 0.3g

Comment: Other pulses and vegetables can be used in this dish.

Lettuce wraps - serves 4, V and NGCI

8 Cos lettuce leaves well washed
50g cooked rice
50g grated carrots
50g chopped plain peanuts
Splash soy sauce (check it is NGCI)

Mix all of the ingredients in a bowl. Spread out the lettuce leaves so that there are 2 per portion. Put the rice and nut and vegetable mixture in the middle and fold round to make a parcel or wrap.

Typical nutritional content per serving kcals 97, carbohydrate 7g, fat 6g, saturated fat 1.2g, salt 0g

Comment: Other nuts, seeds and humus with the rice make interesting fillings.

Blue cheese and walnut salad - serves 4, V and NGCI

2 tablespoons olive oil or rapeseed oil
2 tablespoons lemon juice
100g blue cheese chopped
100g small salad potatoes boiled in their skins
60g chopped walnuts
Half a crispy lettuce chopped
Black pepper

Mix the oil and lemon juice with the black pepper. Toss in the rest of the ingredients.

Typical nutritional content per serving kcals 302, carbohydrate 6g, fat 27g, saturated fat 8.0g, salt 0,5g

Comment: Other cheeses can be used.

Cauliflower cheese - serves 4, V and NGCI

One cauliflower boiled or steamed (frozen can be used)
100g low fat cheese grated (check it is NGCI if already grated and also suitable
for vegetarians)
600ml skimmed milk
4 teaspoons corn flour

Mix a small amount of milk with the corn flour. Boil the milk add the corn flour mix and
stir until thickened. Add the cheese and stir. Pour the sauce over the hot boiled / steamed
cauliflower.

Typical nutritional content per serving kcals 269, carbohydrate 36g, fat 6g, saturated fat
3.0g, salt 0.7g

Comment: For ease, instead of corn flour, thickening granules can be used or even a cheese
sauce mix.

Quinoa and savoury vegetables - serves 4, V and NGCI

300g quinoa
1 tablespoon of olive oil
1 aubergine cut into chunks
1 red pepper cut into strips
1 green pepper cut into strips
2 courgettes cut into chunks
1 red onion cut into chunks
I tablespoon of yeast extract mixed with a little warm water (check it is NGCI)
I tablespoon fresh mixed herbs

Cook the quinoa according to the directions on the packet. Meanwhile spread the olive oil on a baking tray and add the vegetables. Drizzle with the yeast extract mix and sprinkle with herbs. Roast the vegetables at the top of the oven until soft. Top the quinoa with the vegetables.

Typical nutritional content per serving kcals 321, carbohydrate 47g, fat 8g, saturated fat 1.1g, salt 0.4g

Comment: Quinoa is a soft seed which is like grain and originally came from South America. It contains no gluten. It can be used instead of cous cous or rice in dishes. If fresh herbs are not available, use half the quantity of dried ones.

Spicy prawns - serves one, NGCI

75g prawns peeled and deveined if fresh or use ready cooked ones
1 teaspoon oil
1 tablespoon sweet chilli sauce (check it is NGCI)

Mix the oil and chilli sauce together in a bowl, add the prawns. Cover and put in the fridge to marinade for 30 minutes. Heat a little oil in a pan add the prawns and marinade. Cook, until coloured if fresh, and serve.

Typical nutritional content per serving kcals 122, carbohydrate 4g, fat 6g, saturated fat 0.7g, salt 2.0g

Comment: Other sauces can be used instead of the chilli sauce.

Beef burger - serves 4, NGCI

400g lean beef mince
1 tomato chopped
1 tablespoon tomato paste
1 teaspoon paprika - optional

Put the ingredients into a bowl and mix. Divide into 4 portions and flatten into burgers. Put on a plate, cover and allow to set for 5 to10 minutes in the fridge. Put the burgers on a hot pre-heated grill or BBQ and cook for 5-6 minutes each side, checking they are cooked right through.

Typical nutritional content per serving kcals 137, carbohydrate 1g, fat 4g, saturated fat 1.8g, salt 0.2g

Comment: Other meats or poultry can be used to make the burgers.

Roast chicken breast - serves one, NGCI

One chicken breast
Lemon cut into slices
Small amount of oil

Pre-heat the grill. Place the chicken breast on a grill pan spread over the lemon rings. Cook for 15-20 minutes until cooked right through and the juices run clear.

Typical nutritional content per serving kcals 202, carbohydrate 3g, fat 7g, saturated fat 1.1g, salt 0.2g

Comment: Turkey could be used instead. If available, pheasant or pigeon can also be used.

Nut roast - serves 4, V and NGCI

2 medium onions chopped
400ml can chickpeas drained and chopped
125g cooked brown basmati rice
50g brazils roughly chopped (other nuts can be used)
2 teaspoons full yeast extract (check NGCI)
1 teaspoon fresh herbs chopped finely
2 teaspoons of low fat spread (check it is gluten free)
2 eggs lightly beaten
Salt and pepper to taste

Cook the onion in a little water until soft. Mix all of the other ingredients except the eggs. Then add the eggs and mix through. Line a loaf tin with greaseproof paper, well greased with the low fat. Place the mix in the loaf tin and bake in a preheated oven at 190°C, gas mark 5 for 45 minutes or until set. Slice and serve.

Typical nutritional content per serving kcals 310, carbohydrate 27g, fat 15g, saturated fat 3.6g, salt 2g

Comment: To save greasing the tin, use silicon bake ware to release the food more easily.

Baked banana

Baked banana - serves one, V and NGCI

One banana
Squirt of lemon juice

Simply wrap a banana in foil and bake in a hot oven for 5 minutes. This can then be served alone or with an ice cream of whatever type and flavour you enjoy.

Typical nutritional content per serving kcals 95, carbohydrate 22g, fat 0g, saturated fat 0g, salt 0g

Comment: This is such an easy recipe and can be served with ice cream but this will add calories and carbohydrate.

Strawberry blancmange - serves 4 to 6, V and NGCI

600ml of skimmed milk
Sweetener
Packet of blancmange (check it is NGCI)
100g strawberries

Make up the blancmange according to the directions on the packet using skimmed milk and sweetener. Allow to set. Decorate with strawberries and serve.

Typical nutritional content per serving kcals 86, carbohydrate 15g, fat 0g, saturated fat 0g, salt 0.2g

Comment: Other types of blancmange can be used.

Rice pudding - serves 6, V and NGCI

75g short grain rice
Sweetener to taste
850ml skimmed milk
Sprinkle of nutmeg – optional

Preheat oven to 150°C, gas mark 2. Put the rice in a large baking dish, add the milk and sweetener. Sprinkle nutmeg on top. Bake in the centre of the oven for 2 hours. Add extra milk if it becomes dry.

Typical nutritional content per serving kcals 90g, carbohydrate 15g, fat 1g, saturated fat 0.2g, salt 0.2g

Comment: Tapioca can be used instead of rice

Lemon cheesecake - serves 6, V and NGCI

100g digestive biscuits
(gluten free if NGCI required)
50g low fat spread
Sachet of sugar free lemon jelly
(check suitable for vegetarians)
Whipping cream 100g (can use silken tofu)
Plain low fat yoghurt 100g
(check it is NGCI and V or use plain soy dessert)
Sweetener granular or powder to taste
Lemon rind shavings

Dissolve the jelly in a little hot water and allow to cool but not set. Meanwhile, make the base. Crush the biscuits by putting in a bag and running a rolling pin over them. Melt the spread and mix in the biscuit crumbs. Put into a greased tin with a removable base and refrigerate for 10 minutes to set. Whip the cream until stiff, fold in the yoghurt, sweetener and lemon rind to the cooled jelly. Cover and chill for 2 hours. Decorate with lemon rind.

Typical nutritional content per serving kcals 196, carbohydrate 15g, fat 14g, saturated fat 6.5g, salt 0.5g

Comment: Using silken tofu will reduce the fat.

Melon boats - serves 6, V and NGCI

One melon cut into 6 slices
100g raspberries – fresh or frozen
Sweetener
6 scoops vanilla ice cream (check it is NGCI)

Take half of the raspberries and gently stew in a little water until soft and then sieve to make a sauce. Add sweetener to taste. Decorate the melon with a scoop of ice cream, raspberries and sauce.

Typical nutritional content per serving kcals 166, carbohydrate 24g, fat 6g, saturated fat 3.7g, salt 0.3g

Comment: Other types of fruit can be used such as blackcurrants or blackberries.

Snacks

Snacks are useful between meals not only to stave off hunger but also to maintain blood sugar levels.

Food	Kcal	Grams of Carbohydrate
80-100g fresh fruit	40-70	10-15
10 grapes	40	15
Small slice of mango	40	10
80g strips of carrot or celery	20	0-5
1 medium slice of bread	75	15
1 crumpet	90	20
2 plain crackers	95	10
80g tinned sweetcorn	90	20
20g plain popcorn	120	20
2 plain rice cakes	60	15
2 crispbreads	36	10
2 rich tea biscuits	60	10
1 fig roll	80	15
2 digestive biscuits	140	20
2 ginger biscuits	90	15
2 oat cakes	80	10
1 small packet of crisps	150	15
1 small slice of carrot cake	190	20
1 scoop of ice cream	70	10
Small pot low fat yoghurt or fromage frais	70-100	10
300ml semi-skimmed milk	138	15
Cup of lentil or vegetable soup	30-70	10-15

Chapter 10

Snacks, takeaways, eating out and travel

Snacks

Snacks are useful for several reasons:

- to stave off hunger,
- to prevent a 'hypo',
- to maintain blood sugar levels,
- if a meal is delayed, a snack may prevent blood sugars dropping too low,
- alcohol lowers blood sugars, so if drinking alcohol not with a meal, it is sensible to snack at the same time.

Eating out and takeaways

If you are eating out or choosing a takeaway, managing your diet is not as difficult as it may first seem. If you are selecting from a menu, try to choose foods that are low in fat and where you can gauge the carbohydrate content. If you are tempted by fast foods, avoid 'going large' with the meal and ask for extra salad or vegetables rather than fries and choose a low sugar drink.

Eating Italian food

You can choose healthy options in several ways. If you like pizza, then choose one with a thin base rather than thick crust or cheese filled types. If you are eating pasta, then choose a tomato sauce instead of one that is creamy. You can also eat lots of salads.

Eating Indian food

Indian food can be very healthy providing you avoid fried dishes like samosas, bhajees, fried rice and battered food. Curries like Kormas are also high in fat.

It can be easy to eat large amounts of carbohydrate in the form of poppadums and chutneys, followed by a large portion of rice with curry and potato side dishes as well a naan or paratha breads. So here are some tips:

- If you are having poppadums, choose yoghurt based dips like raita rather than large helpings of pickles and chutneys. If you are at home, cook them in a microwave rather than frying them.

- Choose boiled rather than fried rice and enjoy dishes like phalls, tomato based curries and biryanis.

- You can also ask for no extra oil or ghee to be added to the meal.

- Chicken, fish or vegetable dishes are likely to be lower in fat than lamb.

- Chipatis are a better choice than naan or paratha breads.

Eating Chinese food

Chinese dishes like stir fries, curries and chow mein are a better choice than sweet and sour pork or chicken which are coated in batter and deep fried.

Holidays and travel

Whether travelling by car, walking, going on the train or bus, always make sure you have a small snack like a couple of plain biscuits and bottle of water with you. For longer journeys, ensure you have a 'goodie bag' filled with items like drinks, sandwiches and fruit. Not only will this keep you going but it will also save you money and will save you from the temptation of the sweets and chocolate at the service station. It is easy to take:

- A flask of tea or coffee or soup

- Fruit juices diluted with extra water

- Bottles of water

- Low calorie squash

- Casseroles or thick soup in wide neck flasks which are warming in cold weather

- Sandwiches – try to use granary or seeded bread and avoid spread if the filling is moist

- Wraps as an alternative to sandwiches – you can even make unusual wraps by rolling cold ham and chopped salad in a lettuce leaf

- Salads with cous cous, rice or pasta and lots of vegetables

- Fruit salads all chopped up and ready to eat.

Chapter 11

Parties

Ideas to get the taste buds flowing!

Parties and special occasions can be a challenge as food tends to be high in fat and sugar. These recipes are about inspiration, not ones to be followed slavishly but ideas to get the taste buds flowing. If you think they are too different from your normal recipes, then adapt them a little but still move towards a lower fat type of recipe.

If you are providing dishes, remember that many people love traditional foods like shepherd's pie but the knack to making it special is how you serve it. For example, serve the shepherd's pie in individual dishes for a dinner party or for a buffet, serve it in cups with saucers so people can easily hold it for eating. Decorate with herbs. Side salads and vegetables can all provide extra colour. Starters can be soup, paté, filled mushrooms or fruit selections which can be served on attractive dishes and decorated with fruit, herbs, croutons, swirls of plain yoghurt or toasted nuts.

Accompanying bread can be warmed or home baked fresh from the oven. If home baked, consider making small rolls in pots, as plaits or heart shapes. Again decorate with seeds or nuts or toasted grains.

For desserts go to town with decorations like fruit cut into shapes, dipped in a little chocolate or frosted. Nut slivers, coconut or chocolate shavings add extra colour. Extra drama can also be added by using candles or sparklers but remember to use them safely.

So often buffets feature sausage rolls, sandwiches and rich fat nibbles. There is nothing wrong with them for special occasions but they are a bit higher in fat and salt and can be a bit boring. So here are a few low fat ideas. All are calculated so they will give you some idea how to fit them into your diet.

Vegetable Kebabs - serves 12 kebabs, V and NGCI

4 large carrots
24 cherry tomatoes
1 large cucumber

Slice the carrots into thin strips using a cheese slicer the type that cuts very thin slices or you may have a food processor that does this – watch your fingers!

Chop the cucumber into chunks. (You could also make the cucumber into very thin slices). Thread the slices of carrots onto skewers, making loops of them interspersing with cherry tomatoes and cucumber.

Typical nutritional content per kebab: kcal 26, carbohydrate 5g, fat 0g, saturated fat 0g, salt 0g.

Comment: You can put other vegetables or a selection of fruits on skewers or slice up the vegetables and eat with a dipping sauce. Try experimenting. Fruits on skewers make a wonderful centrepiece with the skewers arranged into a pattern with a cabbage as the base. The strawberries were just touched at the tips with chocolate. If you do this, remember that apple, pears and banana will brown, so choose strawberries, pieces of pineapple and melon.

Teriyaki kebabs - serves 12 kebabs, NGCI

450g lean sirloin or rump steak cut into long strips.

For the marinade:
4 tablespoons light soy sauce (check it is NGCI)
1 tablespoon sesame oil
1 tablespoon orange juice
2.5cm piece fresh root ginger, peeled and grated
1 garlic clove peeled and crushed – optional

For the dipping sauce:
100ml prepared plum or sweet chilli sauce
1 tablespoon sesame seeds

Mix all the marinade ingredients together in a small bowl and set aside.

Thread the beef strips on to 12 metal or wooden skewers (previously soaked in water if wooden ones). Place in a shallow dish and pour over the marinade mixture. Cover and marinate in the refrigerator for up to 1 hour. Cook the skewers under a preheated moderate grill according to your preference, turning occasionally. Normally 6 minutes per side for well done. Make up the dipping sauce and drizzle over the cooked kebabs or put in a bowl for dipping.

Typical nutritional content per kebab: kcal 62, carbohydrate 1g, fat 2g, 0.7g saturated fat 0.7g, salt 0.1g.

Comment: These kebabs are mainly protein – really tasty and not high in fat. They are around the same calories as many chocolates but much more filling. Variation – intersperse the beef with vegetables or even use pieces of cooked chicken or leftover turkey.

Hot and tasty potatoes
- serves 12 depending on the size of the potatoes

450g salad potatoes or baby potatoes cut into wedges
Chopped thyme and parsley or any other herbs you fancy.
10ml light soya sauce
10ml sesame oil

Put all the ingredients into a plastic bag, shake well. Place potatoes on a baking tray, lightly oiled or on to grease proof paper and bake at the top of a hot oven.

Typical nutritional content per portion: kcal 35, carbohydrate 6g, fat 1g, saturated fat 0.2g, salt 0g.

Nutty Nibbles – serves 20

100g almonds
100g plain popped corn
1 teaspoon sesame seeds
1 tablespoon honey
1 tablespoon sweet chilli
1 tablespoon sesame oil

Mix the seeds, honey and sweet chilli. Put the oil in a non–stick pan, add the nuts and corn. Add the seeds, honey and sweet chilli mixture. Lightly cook, tossing so the corn and nuts are coated. Place in a dish and serve warm.

Typical nutritional content per portion: kcal 115, carbohydrate 7g, fat 9g, saturated fat 0.8g, salt 0g.

Comment: Pop corn is fabulous as a snack and so easy to make in a pan or popcorn maker. It is lovely warm and perhaps flavoured with a drop of vanilla essence or grated parmesan. It makes a good alternative to crisps and other savoury snacks.

Cucumber pockets - serves 12

1 large cucumber, choose a straight one
50g low fat Philadelphia or other low fat soft cheese
Half a teaspoon paprika

Cut the cucumber into 12 pieces. Hollow out a small piece on one side and fill with the cheese. Sprinkle with paprika.

Typical nutritional content per pocket: kcal 11g, carbohydrate 1g, fat 0g, saturated fat 0g, salt 0g.

Comment: These look really pretty and are virtually carbohydrate free as well as containing few calories. Fillings such as humous or paté can be used as an alternative.

Homemade potato crisps - serves 4

1 large potato cut into thin slices
1 large sweet potato cut into thin slices
1 tablespoon sesame oil
Sprinkle of paprika (optional)

Grease a baking tray with the sesame oil. Add the potatoes. Bake at the top of a hot oven until crisp. Toss around in the oil half way through cooking. Some of the slices will remain soft. Sprinkle over with the paprika – serve while hot.

Typical nutritional content:
kcals 101, carbohydrate 15g,
fat 4g, saturated fat 0.6g,
salt 0g.

Comment: You can use
different mixtures of
vegetables such as carrots,
turnips, butternut squash.

Easy Rocky Road trifle - serves 6

120g raspberries
Raspberry sugar free jelly
2 packets low fat custard
Enough low fat cream spray to cover surface
20g mini meringues and marshmallows

Put 100g raspberries at the bottom of a glass serving dish. Make up the jelly according to the instructions allow to cool. Pour over the fruit. Allow to set in the fridge. Make up the custard according to the instructions, allow to cool a little and pour over the jelly. Allow to set in the fridge. Top with the cream and then decorate with the marshmallows, meringues and raspberries.

Typical nutritional content: kcals 149, carbohydrate 27g, fat 3g, saturated fat 1.9g, salt 0.4g.

Comment: You can use other fruits and different flavoured jellies.

Summer pudding - serves 6

500g mixture of plums, blackberries
(washed), apples peeled and chopped
Sweetener to taste
75ml (3fl oz) water
6 slices wholemeal bread

Gently simmer the fruit with the water and sweetener until soft but not falling apart. Sieve the fruit and retain the juice. Cut the bread into circles for the top and bottom of a 750ml (one and a quarter pint) basin and also in shapes to fit the sides. Dip the bread into the juice and line the bowl. Spoon the fruit into the basin and top with the final slice of bread dipped into the juice. Cover with saucer and a weight so that the bread is pressed into the fruit mixture. Chill overnight. Remove the weights and saucer and invert a deep plate on top and then holding very tightly turn over to slide the pudding from the basin.

Typical nutritional content: kcals 104, carbohydrate 20g, fat 1g, saturated fat 0.2g, salt 0. 5g.

Comment: Use different mixtures of fruits. This is a really useful pudding for using frozen fruits which have been collected during the summer harvest. If you go foraging in hedge rows, the blackberries are free!

Chocolate Beetroot Cake - serves 12

75g cocoa or chocolate drink powder
180g plain flour or use 150g white and 30g wholemeal flour
225g sugar
2 teaspoon baking powder
250g cooked and cooled beetroot
3 large eggs
200ml sunflower oil
1 teaspoon vanilla extract
Icing sugar for dusting

Pre-heat oven to 180°C gas 4. Sift dry ingredients together in a bowl. Puree the beetroot. In a separate bowl mix the eggs one at a time with the oil and vanilla essence, when smooth add the sugar. Add the puree beetroot. Make a well in the middle of the dry ingredients and add the beetroot, oil and sugar mixture. Mix well. Pour into a greased and lined 9inch cake tin. Bake 30-40 minutes or until firm and a skewer inserted in the cake leaves it cleanly. Cool on a rack then dust with icing sugar. The cake can be split and filled, if desired.

Typical nutritional content: kcals 329, carbohydrates 32g, fat 20g, saturated fat 3.3g, salt 0.5g.

Comment: This is quite a fashionable cake which can also be made as small cakes. It provides extra vegetables but obviously contains more fat and carbohydrate so try not to have second helpings.

Succulent carrot cake - serves 12

200g wholemeal flour
100g plain flour
350g sugar
3 large grated carrots
2 teaspoons bicarbonate of soda
2 teaspoons cinnamon
4 large eggs
250ml sunflower oil

For topping (optional)
225g (9oz) icing sugar
Juice from 3 lemons

Pre-heat oven to 180C, gas 4. Sift dry ingredients together in a bowl. Add the grated carrots. Gradually add the oil and eggs. Mix well and pour into a greased and lined 9inch cake tin. Bake 40 to 50 minutes or until firm and a skewer inserted in the cake leaves it cleanly. Cool on a rack. Make the topping with the icing sugar and lemon juice.

Typical nutritional content: kcals 318, carbohydrate 35g, fat 18g, saturated fat 24g, salt 0.4g.

Comment: It is a lovely cake and popular with the whole family but it is higher in fat and carbohydrate than most desserts, so keep it as a treat.

We cannot discuss parties without mentioning alcohol

There is no need for people with diabetes to give up alcohol simply because of their diabetes, especially as this may affect their social life. Alcohol does have an effect on blood sugar levels but with a few precautions people with diabetes can enjoy a drink.

In fact, diabetes alcohol guidelines are the same as for the general population which is 2-3 units for women and 3-4 units for men. However, it is worth being aware how many units a drink contains. Sometimes a glass of wine will contain 2 units and a pint of beer can even reach 3 units. The following website is very useful: https://www.drinkaware.co.uk

What is an alcohol unit?

One unit (approximate measure):

- 1/2 pint of standard strength beer, lager or cider

- 1 pub shot/optic/measure (50ml) of sherry or vermouth

- 1 pub shot/optic/measure of spirit (25 ml), eg gin, vodka or whisky.

- 175ml glass of wine size

People with diabetes need to be extra careful with alcohol

The tendency to low blood sugars (hypoglycaemia) after alcohol can be within 4-6 hours but blood glucose levels can remain low for 24-36 hours after significant alcohol consumption. The carbohydrates that the drink may contain do not offset the blood sugar lowering effect of the alcohol, so do not count these as part of your carbohydrate consumption and assume you will be alright.

In addition to the risk of hypos, alcohol impairs your judgement and if you have diabetes, this means that you may not realise that you are having a hypo and so you will not treat it with sugary food. Furthermore, your friends may not realise that you are hypo and may simply assume that your 'odd' behaviour is because you are drunk. This can be an unsafe situation leading to a severe hypoglycaemic attack.

Precautions

- Only drink in moderation, sensible advice whether you have diabetes or not.

- Do not drink on an empty stomach.

- Learn by experience how alcohol affects you – everyone is different.

- Take the appropriate steps to prevent a hypo and if you are treated with insulin, consider lowering your insulin dose at the meal prior to going out for a drink.

- The best time to drink is with a meal.

- If you are not having a meal with your alcohol, then it is a good idea to nibble carbohydrate [eg crisps] throughout the evening. If a large amount of alcohol is consumed, then even chips or pizza may be considered.

- Have an extra bedtime snack before going to bed to try to avoid a night hypo.

Glossary of terms

A

Acetone: One of the chemicals called ketones. These are produced when there is too little insulin present and the body uses fat for energy. Acetone in the urine usually means that more insulin is needed.

Ace-inhibitors: Drugs that inhibit an enzyme (angiotensin converting enzyme) in the kidneys that increase the blood pressure.

Acidosis: Shifting of the pH in the blood towards being acidic.

Adrenal Gland: Small organ situated above the kidneys that produces a number of different hormones, including adrenaline and cortisol.

Adrenergic symptoms: Bodily symptoms of hypoglycaemia caused mainly by adrenaline.

Albumin: A protein that is in most animal tissues. The presence of albumin in the urine may be a sign of kidney or bladder infection or early kidney damage.

Aldose reductace inhibitors: Drugs that can affect nerve damage caused by diabetes.

All Party Parliamentary Group for Diabetes: To study the condition of diabetes and its clinical and legal complexities.

Alpha cells: Cells in the Islets of Langerhans of the pancreas that produce the hormone glucagon.

Analogue insulin: Insulin made by genetically engineering already genetically engineered human insulin.

Antibodies: Produced by the immune defense system to destroy viruses and bacteria.

Arteriosclerosis: Hardening, narrowing and eventually blocking of the blood vessels.

Aspartame: A low-calorie sweetener. This can have some quite dramatic side effects in some people.

Autonomic Neuropathy: Damage to the system of nerves which regulate many autonomic functions of the body such as stomach emptying, sexual function and blood pressure control.

Autonomic nervous system: The 'independent' part of the nervous system that is operated without having to give it a thought, including things like breathing and the movement of the intestines.

Autoimmune system: Sometimes things go wrong and the cells of the body are attacked eg an infection and the autoimmune system is the body's defense mechanism for fighting off the attack.

B

Basal insulin: A low level of insulin that covers the body's need for insulin between meals and during the night. The insulin is given as intermediate or long-acting insulin.

Basal rate: With an insulin pump, a low dose of basal insulin is infused every hour of the day and night.

Beef insulin: Insulin extracted from the pancreas of cattle, also referred to as bovine insulin.

Beta cells: Cells in the Islets of Langerhans of the pancreas that produce the hormone insulin.

Biguanides: Drugs used to treat Type 2 diabetes.

Blood Glucose Monitoring: A system of measuring blood glucose levels at home using special strips and a meter.

Brittle Diabetes: A term used to describe diabetes which is extremely unstable where blood glucose levels swing from very low to very high.

C

Capillary Blood: The capillaries are the very fine blood vessels between arteries and veins to allow the blood deliveries of oxygen to the tissues. Blood tests from fingers contain capillary blood.

Carbohydrate: A class of food which comprises of starches and sugar that are most easily available by the body for energy. Found in mainly plant foods eg rice, bread, potatoes, pasta and dried beans.

Coeliac disease: Illness where the person cannot tolerate gluten, a substance found in wheat, oats, barley and rye.

Coma: Unconsciousness. Can occur in people with diabetes when the blood glucose is very low (insulin coma) or very high (diabetes coma).

Control: Usually refers to blood glucose control.

Continuous glucose monitor [CGM]: A blood glucose monitor which provides short-term trends in the blood sugar as they happen. It shows the direction your blood glucose levels are taking in the last 1, 3, 6, 9, 12, or 24 hours depending on the type of monitor.

C-peptide: 'Connecting peptide' a hormone produced together with insulin in the beta cells. By measuring C-peptide, the residual insulin production of the pancreas can be estimated.

Cortisol: Stress hormone that is produced in the adrenal gland.

Counter regulation: The body's defense against low levels of blood glucose. The excretion of the counter regulating hormones (glucagon, adrenaline, growth hormone and cortisol) increases when the blood glucose level falls too low.

CSII: Continuous subcutaneous insulin infusion, treatment with an insulin pump.

Cystitis: Inflammation of the bladder causing frequent of passing urine and a burning sensation when passing urine. This should not be confused with frequent passing of urine due to high blood sugars.

D

Dawn phenomenon: The growth hormone level rises during the night, causing the blood glucose level to rise early in the morning.

Depot effect: Part of the insulin that is injected is stored in the fat tissue as a depot (a spare tank of insulin). The longer the action of insulin, the larger the depot.

Dextrose: Pure glucose.

Diabetes/Diabetic Coma: Unconsciousness [coma] that occurs as a result of very high blood glucose levels [hyperglycemia] and is usually accompanied by ketoacidosis.

Diabetes Ketones: Ketones that are produced when the cells in the body are starved of insulin and therefore the blood glucose level is high.

Diabetes mellitus: The full name for 'diabetes', a disorder of the pancreas.

Diabetic amyotrophy: A rare condition causing pain and/or weakness of the legs as a result of nerve damage.

Glossary of terms

Dialysis: The process of extracting harmful substances from the blood when the kidneys no longer can.

DKA: Diabetes ketoacidosis, also called ketoacidosis which is a serious condition due lack of insulin. As a result, body fat is used up to provide energy but dangerous ketones and acids are also formed. It is caused by high blood sugar levels which result in ketones in the urine, vomiting, drowsiness, heavy laboured breathing and breath smelling of acetone [pear drops].

E

Exchanges: Portions of carbohydrate foods in the diabetic diet that can be exchanged for others. One exchange is equal to 10gms of carbohydrate.

F

Fatty Acid: Substances produced when fat is broken down in the body.

Free Food: Foods that contain very little carbohydrate and so can be eaten in liberal amounts by people with diabetes without counting them in their diet. E.g. most vegetables, most salad ingredients, tea, coffee, meat and cheese. Note: meat and cheese are carbohydrate free but contain fats.

Fructose: A type of sugar found naturally in fruit and honey. It does not require insulin for its metabolism and so is often used as a sweetener in food for people with diabetes.

G

Gastroparesis: Slow stomach emptying, a complication of diabetes caused by neuropathy

Galactose: Sugar molecule. Lactose consists of galactose and glucose.

Gestational diabetes: Diabetes occurring during pregnancy. The symptoms disappear after childbirth but the woman has an increased risk of acquiring Type 2 diabetes later in life.

Gluconeogenesis: Production of sugar in the liver.

Glucagon: A hormone produced by the pancreas which causes a rise in blood glucose by freeing glycogen from the liver. It is available as an injection to treat a severe hypo when food or drink cannot be administered.

Glucose: A form of sugar made by digestion of carbohydrates. Absorbed into the bloodstream where it circulates and is used for energy.

Glucose tolerance test: Test to diagnose early stages of diabetes. Tells how much the blood glucose level rises after orally ingested or intravenously given glucose.

Gluten: Compound that makes dough sticky. Found in wheat, oats, rye and barley.

Glycaemic index: A method of classifying carbohydrates and foods according to how they affect the body glucose level. Abbreviates to GI.

Glycated haemoglobin [HbA1c]: The part of the haemoglobin that has glucose attached to it. The measurement of HbA1c gives the average glucose level over the last 6 to 8 weeks.

Glycogen: The form in which carbohydrate is stored in the liver. It is often known as animal starch.

Glycogenolysis: The breakdown of the glycogen store in liver or muscles.

Glycosuria: Presence of glucose in the urine.

Goitre: Enlarged thyroid gland

Growth hormone: Hormone that is produced in the pituitary gland. Increased growth is the most important effect. It increases the blood glucose level.

H

HbA1c: Blood test that measures how much glucose binds to red blood cells over a 6 to 8 week period.

Haemoglobin A1: The part of the haemoglobin of the red blood cell to which glucose attaches. It is a test of 'diabetes control' as it measures the amount of haemoglobin A1 attached to the red cells so giving the average blood glucose levels over the 6 to 8 weeks.

Honeymoon Period: Usually only a short time after diagnosis and the start of insulin treatment – the dose of insulin drops due to partial recovery of insulin secretion by the pancreas.

Hormone: Substance generated in a gland or organ which is carried by the blood to another part of the body to stimulate another organ into activity. Insulin is a hormone.

Human insulin: Insulin made by genetic engineering.

Hyperglycaemia: High blood sugars.

Hypoglycaemia: Low blood sugars, also called a 'hypo'

Hypo unawareness: A condition where there are no warning symptoms of impending hypoglycaemia.

I

IDDM: Insulin dependent diabetes mellitus, former name for Type 1 diabetes.

Immune defence: The defence in the body against foreign substances, such as bacteria and virus.

Insulin: A hormone produced by the beta cells of the pancreas which is responsible for the control of glucose in the blood. Insulin can only be given by injection because the digestive juices destroy its action if taken by mouth.

Insulin antibodies: Antibodies in the blood that bind insulin. The insulin that is bound has no function but can be released at a later time when the concentration of insulin in the blood is lower.

Insulin Dependent Diabetes (IDD): The type of diabetes that has to be treated with insulin because the body's pancreas no longer produces it. Most common in younger people. It is also called Type1 diabetes or juvenile-onset diabetes.

Insulin Pen: An injection device for insulin. The injection of insulin is given after dialling the dose and pressing a button.

Insulin Pump: Insulin is infused into the subcutaneous tissue through a thin tubing continuously during day and night.

Insulin Reaction: Another word for low blood sugars or hypoglycaemia, often called a hypo. In some countries it is called 'insulin shock' or 'shock'.

Insulin receptor: Structure on the cell surface to which insulin binds. Initiates the signal that opens the cell membrane for glucose transportation.

Insulin resistance: Decreased insulin sensitivity. A higher level of insulin than normal is needed to obtain the same blood glucose lowering effect.

Intermediate-acting insulin: Insulin that has an effective time action of 8-12 hours, often given twice daily to provide 24 hour insulin cover.

Intradermal: Means 'into the skin'. Usually refers to an injection given into the most superficial layer of skin. Insulin must not be given in this way as it will not be absorbed properly.

Intravenous injection: Injection directly into a vein.

Islet of Langerhans: The cells within the pancreas that produce insulin and glucagon.

J

Juvenile diabetes: Diabetes in childhood and adolescence, another term for type 1 diabetes.

K

Ketoacidosis: A serious condition due lack of insulin which results in body fat being used up to provide energy but dangerous ketones and acids are also formed. It is caused by high blood sugar levels which result in ketones in the urine, vomiting, drowsiness, heavy laboured breathing and breath smelling of acetone [pear drops].

Ketones: Acid substances formed when body fat is used up to provide energy.

Ketosis: Increased amounts of ketones in the blood.

Ketonuria: The presence of acetone and other ketones in the urine. Detected by testing with a special testing stick or tablets. Ketones in the urine are due to lack of insulin or periods of starvation.

Glossary of terms

L

Lactose: Milk sugar.

LADA: Latent Autoimmune Diabetes in the Adult. Onset of Type 1 diabetes after the age of 35, usually with not so dramatic symptoms.

Langerhans: The scientist who discovered the islets of Langerhans in the pancreas in 1869.

Laser Treatment: A process in which laser beams are used to treat a damaged retina.

Lipoathrophy: Loss of fat from the injection sites. More common in the past when insulins were not highly purified.

Lipohypertrophy: Fatty swelling usually caused by repeated injections of insulin into the same place.

Long-acting insulin: Insulin with a prolonged action, up to 24 hrs.

M

Macroangiopathy: Diabetes complications in the large blood vessels.

Metabolism: Process by which the body turns food into energy.

Metabolic syndrome: A group of problems, Type 2 diabetes, high blood pressure, central obesity, high cholesterol; levels and coronary heart disease.

Microalbuminuria: Small amount of protein in the urine. The first sign of kidney damage which can be caused by long term-diabetes.

Microaneurysm: Small protuberances on the retinal vessels. The first stage of eye damage which can be caused by long-term diabetes.

Microangiopathy: Diabetes complications in the small blood vessels of the eye, kidney and nerves.

Millimoles: Unit for measuring the concentration of glucose and other substances in the blood. Blood glucose is measured in millimoles per litre (mmol/l).

Multiple injection treatment: Treatment with injections of short or rapid- acting insulin before meals and intermediate or long-acting insulin to cover day and night.

N

Necrobiosis lipoidica diabeticorum: A special type of skin lesion that can be seen in people with diabetes.

Nephropathy: Kidney damage. In the early stages this makes the kidneys leaky so that albumin appears in the urine. At the later stage it may affect the function of the kidney and in severe cases lead to kidney failure.

Neuroglycopenic symptoms: Symptoms of brain dysfunction caused by a low blood glucose level.

Neuropathy: Damage to the nerves. This may be peripheral or autonomic and is usually caused by long-term diabetes,

NICE: This is the National Institute for Health and Clinical Excellence. NICE is an independent organisation responsible for providing national guidelines for the treatment of various conditions, the use of medicines and on the promotion of good health. www.nice.org.uk

P

Pancreas: A gland lying behind the stomach which secretes digestive fluid and also contains the islets of Langerhans that produce insulin.

Pituitary gland: Small gland situated in the brain where many of the most important hormones in the body are produced.

Pre-meal injection: Injection with short or rapid-acting insulin prior to a meal.

Protamine: A protein from salmon that is added to insulin to extend its action time.

Polydipsia: Being excessively thirsty and drinking too much. Also a symptom of untreated diabetes.

Polyuria: The passing of large quantities of urine due to excess glucose in the bloodstream. It is a symptom of untreated diabetes.

Pork insulin: Insulin derived from the pancreas of pigs, also referred to as porcine insulin.

Proteinuria: Protein or albumin in the urine.

R

Receptor: A special structure on the cell surface that fits with a hormone. The hormone must fit into the receptor for it to have its effect on the cell.

Rebound phenenomenon: After a hypo episode, the blood glucose may rise to high levels. This is caused both by the secretion of counterregulatory hormones and by eating too much when feeling hypo.

Renal Threshold: The level of glucose in the blood above which it will begin to spill into the urine. The renal threshold for glucose in the blood is about 10 mmol/l but this can vary amongst individuals.

Retinopathy: Damage to the retina, the sensitive area at the back of the eye providing sight.

S

Short-acting insulin: Soluble insulin without additives to prolong its action.

Somogyi phenomenon: A special type of rebound phenomenon after a night hypo resulting in high blood glucose levels in the morning.

Sorbitol: Sugar alcohol, a sweetener that gives energy.

Starch: Complex carbohydrates found in potatoes, corn, rice and wheat.

Subcutaneous Injection: An injection beneath the skin into the layer of fat which lies between the skin and muscle – where insulin should be injected.

Sucrose: Cane or beat sugar, brown sugar, table sugar, powder sugar, and saccharose.

Sulponylureas: Drugs used to treat Type 2 diabetes by stimulating the beta cells in the pancreas to more insulin eg tolbutamide, gliclazide.

T

Type 1 Diabetes: Another name for insulin dependent diabetes, the type that is always treated with insulin.

Type 2 Diabetes: Another name for non-insulin dependent diabetes which may be treated with diet only, diet and tablets and eventually insulin if the other treatments fail.

Thiazoidinediones: Drugs to treat Type 2 diabetes by reducing insulin resistance.

U

U 100: The standard strength of insulin in the UK and many other countries.

Unaware hypo: A hypo without having had warning symptoms associated with decreasing blood sugar.

V

Visual acuity: The measurement of vision by reading letters on a chart.

Visual field: The measurement of the area that can be seen while the eyes are looking straight ahead – important for driving.